BTEC Tech Award

ENGINEERING

Student Book

Simon Goulden

Edited by Katy Archer and Gary Blogg

Published by Pearson Education Limited, 80 Strand, London, WC2R 0RL.

www.pearsonschoolsandfecolleges.co.uk

Copies of official specifications for all Pearson qualifications may be found on the website: qualifications.pearson.com

Text © Pearson Education Limited, 2017

Subject advisor Stephen Singleton

Designed by Colin Tilley Loughrey

Typeset by Tech Set

Original illustrations © Pearson Education Limited, 2017

Illustrated by Tech Set

Cover photo/illustration © Creativa Images/Shutterstock.com; luckyraccoon/Alamy Stock Photo

The right of Simon Goulden to be identified as author of this work has been asserted by him in accordance with the Copyright, Designs and Patents Act 1988.

First published 2018

21 20 19 18
10 9 8 7 6 5 4 3 2 1

British Library Cataloguing in Publication Data
A catalogue record for this book is available from the British Library

ISBN 9781292218922

Printed in Slovakia by Neografia.

Acknowledgements
The author and publisher would like to thank the following individuals and organisations for permission to reproduce copyright material.

Photographs

(Key: b-bottom; c-centre; l-left; r-right; t-top)

123RF: Turmfalke 003, Blazej Lyjak 005r, Unlim3d 012, Wodthikorn Phutthasatchathum 021, Mikhail Starodubov 029, Arnoaltix 033, Maruna Skoropadska 061, Stuart Miles 073, Luchschen 074, Hywit Dimyadi 080, Manfredxy 083, Ivan Trifonenko 090, Alexander Sorokopud 100, Srapulsar38 101, Andrey Radchenko 124, Videodoctor 146, Aleksandr Vinokurov 167, Ensup 207, Winai Tepsuttinun 210, Luminis 220; **Alamy Stock Photo:** B Christopher 005l, Antony Nettle 014, Dejan Jekic 025, Agencja Fotograficzna Caro 027, Dimitri Stangl 046, Leonid Shtandel 067, Daniel Barquero 106, Juha Jarvinen 111, Aykut Erdogdu 125, Dpa Picture Alliance 206; **Corbis:** Monty Rakusen/Cultura 164; **Pearson Education Ltd:** Jules Selmes 093; **Photodisc:** 82r; **Shutterstock:** Rainer Plendl 019, Dmitry Kalinovsky 026, Phovoir 030, Sofist 042, Blend Images 044, Dustie 048, Marekusz 062, Ronfromyork 066, Nikkolia 077, DJ Srki 082l, Photosync 084, Aleksandr Kurganov 091, Luchschen 097l, Stillfx 097r, Furtseff 113, Tomas Mikula 141, Shooarts 142, Deymos Photo 145, Tomas Mikula 147, Yomka 148, Blazej Lyjak 149, Inozemtsev Konstantin 151, Zhukov Oleg 160, 162, Ryan Carter 178, Mikhail Bakunovich 180, Sebastian Kaulitzki 182l, HYPERLINK "https://premier.shutterstock.com/image/contributor/1600454" Ksander 182r, Alex Helin 184l, Jon Le-Bon 184r, Coprid 186, Georgi Roshkov 192, Hxdbzxy 193, Olena Zaskochenko 204, Stephane Bidouze 208, Michaeljung 225, Fernando Blanco Calzada 227

All other images © Pearson Education

Pearson Education Limited is not responsible for the content of any external internet sites. It is essential for tutors to preview each website before using it in class so as to ensure that the URL is still accurate, relevant and appropriate. We suggest that tutors bookmark useful websites and consider enabling students to access them through the school/college intranet.

Notes from the publisher
1.
In order to ensure that this resource offers high-quality support for the associated Pearson qualification, it has been through a review process by the awarding body. This process confirms that this resource fully covers the teaching and learning content of the specification or part of a specification at which it is aimed. It also confirms that it demonstrates an appropriate balance between the development of subject skills, knowledge and understanding, in addition to preparation for assessment.

Endorsement does not cover any guidance on assessment activities or processes (e.g. practice questions or advice on how to answer assessment questions), included in the resource nor does it prescribe any particular approach to the teaching or delivery of a related course.

While the publishers have made every attempt to ensure that advice on the qualification and its assessment is accurate, the official specification and associated assessment guidance materials are the only authoritative source of information and should always be referred to for definitive guidance.

Pearson examiners have not contributed to any sections in this resource relevant to examination papers for which they have responsibility.

Examiners will not use endorsed resources as a source of material for any assessment set by Pearson.

Endorsement of a resource does not mean that the resource is required to achieve this Pearson qualification, nor does it mean that it is the only suitable material available to support the qualification, and any resource lists produced by the awarding body shall include this and other appropriate resources.

2.
Pearson has robust editorial processes, including answer and fact checks, to ensure the accuracy of the content in this publication, and every effort is made to ensure this publication is free of errors. We are, however, only human, and occasionally errors do occur. Pearson is not liable for any misunderstandings that arise as a result of errors in this publication, but it is our priority to ensure that the content is accurate. If you spot an error, please do contact us at resourcescorrections@pearson.com so we can make sure it is corrected.

Contents

CONTENTS

About this book

This book is designed to support you when you are taking a BTEC Tech Award in Engnieering.

About your BTEC Tech Award

Congratulations on choosing a BTEC Tech Award in Engineering. This exciting and challenging course will introduce you to the engineering sector, which covers a wide range of rapidly developing areas such as renewable energy, low carbon, aerospace, automotive, and bioscience. By studying for your Award you will gain important knowledge and technical skills within a practical learning environment.

This book will support you in the four engineering areas of equal importance, which cover:

- the development of key practical and technical engineering skills, such as research, observation, measurement, making, using computer-aided design (CAD) and disassembly
- knowledge of key engineering sectors (mechanical, electrical/electronic and engineering design) and the interrelation of each in the industry
- knowledge of the stages involved in planning and implementing an engineering project
- knowledge and skills involved in the investigation of solutions to engineering problems in response to a given brief.

How you will be assessed

You will be assessed in two different ways. Components 1 and 2 are assessed through internal assessment. This means that your teacher will give you an assignment brief and indicate to you the deadline for completing it. The assignment will cover what you have been learning about and will be an opportunity to apply your knowledge and skills. You teacher will mark your assignment and award you with a grade. Your third assessment (for Component 3) will be an external assessment. This will be a task that is set and marked by Pearson. You will have a set time in which to complete this task. The task will be an opportunity to bring together what you have learnt in Components 1 and 2.

How to use this book

The book has been designed in a way that will help you to easily navigate through your course. Each component from the course is covered in a separate chapter that makes clear what you are learning and how this will contribute to your assessment. There are opportunities for you to test your understanding of key areas, as well as activities that will challenge and extend your knowledge and skills. You will get the most from this book if you use each feature as part of your study. The different features will also help you develop the skills that will be important in completing your assignments as well as preparing you for your external assessment.

Features of the book

This book is designed in spreads, which means that each pair of facing pages represents a topic of learning. Each spread is about 1 hour of lesson time. Your teacher may ask you to work through a spread during a lesson or in your own time. Each spread contains a number of features that will help you to check what you are learning and offer opportunities to practise new skills.

Getting started A short activity or discussion that will introduce you to what you will be covering in the lesson.

Activity These will help you learn about the topic. You may be asked to work in pairs, groups or on your own.

Key terms Important words or terms are defined.

Check my learning This is an opportunity to check back over what you have learnt. It may be a discussion or homework activity.

At the end of each learning aim there is a section that outlines how you will be
assessed and provides opportunities for you to build skills for assessment.

Checkpoint This feature is designed
to allow you to assess your learning.
The 'strengthen' question helps
you to check your knowledge and
understanding of what you have
been studying, while the 'challenge'
questions are an opportunity to
extend your learning.

Assessment Activity This is a practice
assessment that reflects the style and
approach of an assignment brief. In
Component 3, tasks in the assessment
activity features will be similar to those you
should expect in your external assessment.

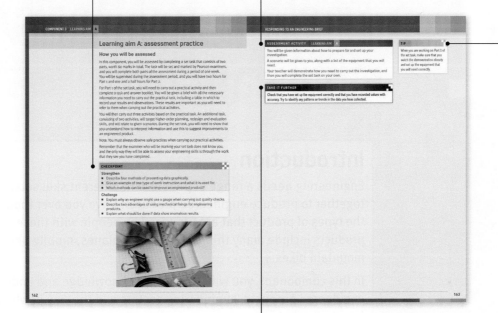

Tip A hint
or tip that
will help you
with your
assessment.

Take it further This provides
suggestions for what you can do to
further the work you've done in the
practice assessment.

1

Exploring Engineering Sectors and Design Applications

Introduction

Engineering needs a range of people with different skill sets, working together to produce engineered products. Have you ever thought about the types of product that are produced by people with these skills? These products include many things – cars, aeroplanes, mobile phones and mountain bikes.

In this component, you will develop your knowledge and understanding of engineered products, engineering sectors and the way in which they are interconnected.

Consider how engineers solve real-life problems, such as modifying existing and developing new products. The development of a smart watch is a typical example – many different engineers will have been involved in developing and creating this innovative technology, including people within the electronic engineering sector. Can you think of any other engineering sectors that may have contributed to the development of this product?

You will also explore engineering skills through the design process, learn about the role of designers in the production of engineered products, and begin to understand how and why they use their knowledge. You will complete practical exercises to produce solutions to problems using a combination of engineering skills – for example, by producing sketches, 2D CAD drawings and physical 3D models.

LEARNING AIMS

In this component you will:

A	understand engineering sectors, products and organisations, and how they interrelate
B	explore engineering skills through the design process.

What is engineering?

KEY TERMS

Products are things produced for sale, usually by a manufacturing process.

Services are the actions of providing something for a customer, usually performing work or a process.

Engineered products are items produced using suitable engineering production processes.

Lathes are tools that rotate a workpiece to perform functions such as shaping, cutting and sanding.

Milling machines are also used to shape materials, but the material is fixed and the cutting tool rotates.

Engineering has a broad range of definitions and can be divided into many disciplines and sub-disciplines. As a branch of science and technology, engineering is the application of mathematical and scientific principles to develop solutions for **products** and **services**, often involving activities associated with innovation, and research and development (R&D).

In the context of **engineered products**, a general definition for engineering is 'the safe application of technical and practical knowledge to transform ideas and materials (as part of a team) into products'. In practical terms, this means that engineering covers the development and creation of new products that can be used across many parts of everyday life.

DID YOU KNOW?

Engineering can be traced back through history. In ancient Egypt, the construction of the pyramids required levers, pulleys, mechanisms and other engineering devices. The Romans took these principles even further, building aqueducts and sewers, and military weapons such as catapults.

Engineering disciplines

There are four main engineering disciplines or areas of study:

- Mechanical engineering studies the design, manufacture and use of machines. This includes everything from the design of small parts, like springs, to complex workshop machinery such as **lathes** and **milling machines**.

- Electrical engineering studies the practical applications of electricity and magnetism. This includes everything from the electronic circuits in your mobile phone to the generators and control systems used in large power stations.

- Civil engineering studies the design, planning and construction of large scale structures such as bridges, building or tunnels.

- Chemical engineering studies the processes and equipment needed to manufacture chemical products on a large scale. This includes everything from shampoo to petrol.

There are also sub-disciplines of these main disciplines. Automotive engineering, for example, is a sub-discipline of mechanical engineering.

All engineering disciplines employ many types of trained and qualified engineer who have specialist skills and knowledge.

ACTIVITY

Search online and watch a video explaining what engineering is about and how it is used in everyday life, making notes that you can then compare and discuss with your group.

Engineering achievements

There are many engineering achievements that have helped people in their everyday lives, and more specific developments that have helped particular groups of people.

How would the British cycling team have won so many gold medals at both the Rio and London Summer Olympic Games without the support of engineers? The team did not ride regular bikes or wear regular clothing. Instead, they had engineered products specifically developed to make them go faster. This included clothing, using **nanotechnology**, and composite bike frames and helmets that were lightweight but strong and had lower resistance to drag. All of these engineered products helped the team win their races.

Auto engineers in Formula One racing fine tune racing cars for optimum speed and performance. The techniques used are passed on to major car manufacturers, who develop them for the everyday family car.

Global positioning systems (GPS) were developed for military operations. However, they are now used daily by millions of people across the world. When GPS systems were commercially introduced in 1989, they were the size and weight of several bricks. Now they have been incorporated into wearable technology, such as in fitness watches that help athletes track how far they have run, as well as in smartphones for security ('Find My Phone' technology).

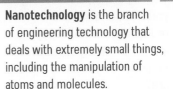

KEY TERM

Nanotechnology is the branch of engineering technology that deals with extremely small things, including the manipulation of atoms and molecules.

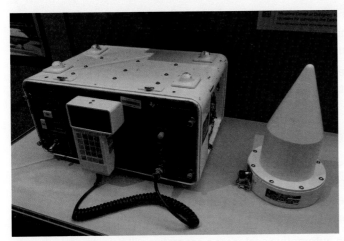

◼ **Original GPS: the size of a suitcase**

◼ **Golf GPS wristwatch: much more lightweight**

ACTIVITY

Can you think of a new engineering invention that could be useful in the future? Compare your ideas with those of others in the group.

CHECK MY LEARNING

You have learned what engineering is, its main disciplines, and why it is important. But unless engineering practices are carried out correctly, things can go seriously wrong.

Watch a video clip on the internet showing examples where engineering designs have failed. Can you think of any instances where this has happened and why?

The need for engineers

Engineering provides employment to many millions of people across the world, enabling a range of products to be designed, made, transported, operated and serviced. Technological progress is rapid and engineering industries are constantly evolving, developing new products that require new processes and skills to design and make.

Engineers need to be flexible and be willing to learn about new technology throughout their careers.

Types of engineer

As you might expect, with there being many engineering disciplines and associated specialties, there are many types of engineers working industry. The list of types of engineers, what they do and the industries they work in is very long.

However, something they have all in common is that they will have completed training and education in their chosen area. They will understand the scientific principles involved and have the skills they need to carry out engineering tasks and solve real-world problems.

Engineering interconnections

More and more, engineers trained in one engineering discipline need to be able to understand other disciplines. The development of many of today's engineered products means that there are now many **interconnections** needed between engineering disciplines for them to work well.

An engineer working in the automotive sector for a car maker will have to understand:

- **mechanical engineering**, to design parts like engines and structural components
- **electrical engineering**
- **electronics engineering**, to control how many of the complex mechanical systems like the engines work
- **computer engineering**, which supports all other disciplines, looking after computer hardware and writing software programs, such as those used to control production processes and purchasing stock levels
- **maintenance engineers** who maintain and service machines and repair equipment when there are breakdowns.

Figure 1.1 shows an example of the kinds of interconnection linking the fuel refining and automotive industries.

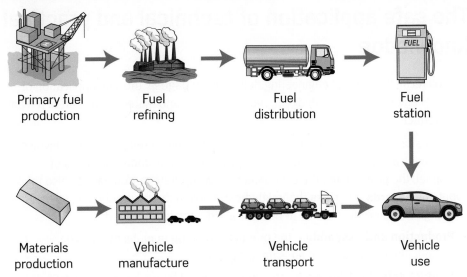

| Primary fuel production | Fuel refining | Fuel distribution | Fuel station |

| Materials production | Vehicle manufacture | Vehicle transport | Vehicle use |

◘ Figure 1.1: Linking the different processes for the manufacture of fuel and a motor vehicle

Why are more engineers needed?

Over time, the UK and many other countries have not trained enough engineers. It is currently estimated that there is a shortage of 69,000 engineers in the UK.

There is also a European shortage of skilled technicians and professional engineers. Olof Persson, the then chief executive of the Volvo Group, said that 'by 2025, we (Europe) might need 500,000 engineers'. In comparison, India and China are currently educating 500,000 engineers annually.

In today's engineering world, the issue of personnel who are not multi-skilled, is of even greater significance to employers. There is an ever-increasing need for people with expertise in more than one engineering discipline, who can then cross boundaries within the engineering industry. For example, an electrical engineer who can support and solve electronics engineering problems is of great benefit to an engineering company.

The safe application of technical and practical knowledge

You will recall the general engineering definition on page 4: 'the safe application of technical and practical knowledge to transform ideas and materials (as part of a team) into products'.

This 'transformation' of ideas and materials into an engineered product can involve many stages and processes. At each stage, you must think about the safety of personnel, the product and the environment it will operate in. You have to also think about any **hazards** and **risks** that might be a problem during production, so that the final engineered product is safe to use and accidents are prevented.

- **Production and assembly** – the product should be manufactured using engineering processes that are safe to carry out.
- **Product delivery/transport** – the product should be packaged or boxed for delivery, and then be unpacked safely when delivered, so that it does not get damaged and become unsafe when operated.
- **Production operation** – there should be a safe way of installing or setting up the product ready for use.
- **Maintenance and disposal** – the product must be safe to clean, repair and maintain, and the process of safe disposal must also be considered.

The engineers of each engineering function need the technical and practical knowledge to be able to deal with safety-related matters at the stages they are involved with. This also includes making the right decisions during the design of the product.

Designing for safety

Product designs should be assessed to avoid hazards and risks. For example, it would be considered unsafe to design a screwdriver with very sharp edges. Aesthetically, it may look good, but it would not be practical or 'fit for purpose' and would also be very unsafe to use.

When designing an engineered product, it is essential to consider the safety not only of the product's intended end user, but also of everyone involved in the making of the product.

How an engineered product can be made safely is an important part of the design. Manufacturing and assembly instructions will be formed from design drawings and information. Right from the start, the design needs to consider what equipment and which materials are needed, and how these can be used safely to make the product. For example, if a component is to be machined on a milling machine that has a safety guard, the component needs to be of a size that fits the machine with the safety guard closed.

Safety in practical working areas

Engineers often work in teams, which means that the potential for safety issues is increased. Not only are you looking after yourself, but there are also other people to consider.

Engineering workshops are a potentially dangerous working environment, so safety awareness is critical. Before any work is carried out, a **risk assessment** of the work area and the processes to be used should be carried out.

Your teacher may have already carried out a risk assessment for the work areas you will be using. If possible, look at this, and make sure you understand it.

Never use any equipment, tools or machinery without first being shown how to use them safely and correctly.

KEY TERM

Risk assessment is a process used to document that all hazards have been considered and appropriate measures put in place to deal with them.

Responsibilities for safety

Everyone has a legal duty of care to look after themselves and others, including while designing a product for others to use or working in an engineering environment. The Health and Safety Executive (HSE) enforces regulatory health and safety standards that all workplaces and employees must follow in order to prevent accidents and injuries in the workplace, whether it be an office, a factory workshop or a building site.

DID YOU KNOW?

The HSE, via the law courts, has prosecuted companies that have broken health and safety laws and has issued them with fines in excess of a million pounds.

LINK IT UP

Go to Component 2 for a list of safety precautions for an engineering workshop.

ACTIVITY

Can you think of something you have seen in a product, in a building, on a building site, or even while walking down the street that you thought was unsafe? Make a list and then discuss within your class.

Search online and find videos that illustrate the causes of some accidents.

CHECK MY LEARNING

You have been introduced to why safety is critical in engineering.

Answer the following revision questions.

1 What is a risk?

2 What is a hazard?

3 Where might there be potential risks and hazards in the engineering process?

Engineering sectors

 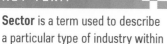
Each engineering **sector** employs engineers from many of the engineering disciplines. This can include designing, developing, manufacturing and selling engineered products.

An engineered product could be a complete motor vehicle, communication systems or even small components used across many of the sectors, e.g. nuts and bolts.

Aerospace

Aerospace engineering is involved with the development of aircraft (aeronautical engineering) and spacecraft (astronautical engineering). Products include aeroplanes, satellites and missiles, and the equipment and systems used in these. Avionics is also related to this sector and deals with the internal electrical and electronics systems of aircraft. Companies within the aerospace engineering sector include BAE Systems and Rolls-Royce.

> ### DID YOU KNOW?
>
> The UK aerospace industry is the second largest in the world after that of the United States.

Automotive

The automotive engineering sector deals with the production of vehicles such as cars, motorbikes (including those for high-performance motorsports), vans, trucks, buses, tractors and other agricultural machinery. Automotive engineers work on all aspects of the design, development and production of these vehicles and their parts and subsystems. Companies within the automotive engineering sector include Ford and Volvo.

Communications

The communications sector is concerned with the design and development of communication networks for voice, data and multimedia applications. This covers mainly internet and computing technologies, networking and telecommunications, and radio. Communications sector companies include BT and Nokia.

Electrical/electronics

The electrical/electronics engineering sector is broad and is connected to many other sectors. Electrical engineers focus on the design and development of electrical control systems and equipment, such as in power and lighting systems for buildings. Electronics engineers specialise more in the design of electronic circuits found in many consumer products. Sector companies include Dyson and Samsung.

Mechanical

The mechanical engineering sector is extremely broad and is also connected to many other sectors. Mechanical engineers provide solutions to problems associated with small components and equipment, as well as larger systems and machines, working on all stages of a product's design and manufacture. Sector companies include Rolls-Royce and GKN.

Environmental

Environmental engineering looks at how the environment is affected by global warming and air pollution. Engineers look at ways that we can protect and improve our environment, including material **recycling**, treatment and reducing waste, as well as control over local and national water supplies.

There are many companies in this sector, perhaps not as well known by name as those in other sectors, including main utility providers.

Transport

The transport sector, also known as transportation engineering, looks after the planning, design and management of the nation's highways and methods of transport, as well as the safe and efficient movement of people and goods/products. The sector has strong links to the structural and rail engineering sectors. Companies in this sector include Atkins and Arup.

Rail

The rail sector is responsible for the maintenance and improvement of the nation's railways. This includes a programme of continuous upgrading of an ageing railway infrastructure as well as maintenance of the systems, train engines and rolling stock used to carry people and goods around the UK. This sector has strong links to both the mechanical and the electrical sectors. Sector companies include Transport for London and Alstom.

DID YOU KNOW?

The UK's railway network has a total length of 9,817 miles.

Marine

The marine sector looks after the engineering associated with ships, boats and other maritime vessels. The sector is also involved with the design, construction and operation of the power plants that drive these vessels, as well as mechanical equipment and systems used at sea harbours and docks and on oil rigs. Sector companies include BAE Systems Maritime and Cummins Engines.

ACTIVITY

1 Did you notice that some companies work in more than one sector? In your class, discuss why this might be.

2 Find and watch some online videos that explain further one or two of the sectors described.

3 Research online to see if you can find other engineering sectors. Make a list of these, noting what each sector covers, and share this with your class group.

CHECK MY LEARNING

You have learned about some of the main engineering sectors. List four of these sectors and find names of two other companies in each of these sectors.

Engineered products

GETTING STARTED

Find photographs of six engineered products. You can use the internet, newspapers and magazines to do this. Which sectors do you think are involved in producing these products?

Many engineered products and systems are assembled from individual components that have been produced by different manufacturers – a combination of engineering products and systems from different engineering sectors.

Engineered products from different sectors

Some engineering companies specialise in the manufacture of one type of engineered product, and so confine their work to one specific engineering sector. An engineering manufacturer that machines component parts for car engines is an example of a company working in the mechanical engineering sector, supplying an engine manufacturer in the automotive engineering sector.

◻ A sports car

Engineered products from combinations of sectors

There are also engineering companies that work across more than one engineering sector. This is often because they produce more than one type of engineered product or engineered system, and these products and systems can be classified in different engineering sectors.

Advances in materials technology and modern manufacturing processes, along with the employment of engineers with knowledge and training in more than one engineering discipline, have made this possible.

A very complex product like a family car has many components from many engineering sectors. These include engineered products from the automotive, mechanical, electronic and environmental sectors. For example:

- From the automotive sector: assemblies such as engines, gearbox, suspension and braking systems.
- From the mechanical sector: engineered component parts for engines, gearbox, suspension and braking systems; body shell parts.
- From the electronics sector: audio and communication systems, engine management systems, GPS systems.
- From the environmental sector: catalytic convertors.

There are many more interconnections. For example, the car's GPS could also be categorised within the communications sector.

Cars contain approximately 30,000 parts or products (if you count every screw, washer, etc.).

Table 1.1 shows some examples of engineered products made in the different engineering sectors.

▣ Table 1.1: Engineered products made in the main sectors

Engineering sector	Engineered products
Aerospace	Engines, wings, rotor blades, landing gears, **fuselages**, navigation systems
Automotive	Engines, suspension systems, braking systems, fuel injection systems, engine management systems, cruise control systems
Communications	Satellite dishes, smartphones, wireless routers, transmission masts, set-top boxes
Electrical/electronic	Drones, televisions, games consoles, wireless speakers/ headphones, smartphones
Mechanical	Gears, shafts, bearings, couplings, hydraulics, pneumatics
Environmental	Photovoltaic cells, wind turbines, wave power capture systems, recycling equipment
Transport	Traffic control systems, road and railway bridges, airport runways, shipping containers
Rail	Rail vehicles, track construction, overhead electrical lines, third rail systems, signalling systems
Marine	Ships, boats, submarines, yachts

KEY TERM

The **fuselage** is the main body of an aircraft, where passengers sit or freight is carried.

ACTIVITY

1 Think of some other engineered products for the sectors listed in Table 1.1. Produce a similar table and list at least four more products for each engineering sector.

2 Using the example of the sports car, think of other engineered products used in car assembly that are produced by each of the engineering sectors. Are any other engineering sectors involved? Make a list of these and discuss with a partner.

CHECK MY LEARNING

There are also other engineering sectors that produce engineered products. Can you find one and the engineered products it produces? Discuss with others in your class.

You have now completed your introduction to engineering sectors, engineered products and the interconnections. Is there anything you are unsure about or need to revise? List the topics you understand and those you do not, ready for discussion at the start of the next lesson.

Engineering organisations: large

Engineering organisations are usually classified as either large enterprises or small and medium-sized enterprises (SMEs).

- Large engineering enterprises, such as motor vehicle manufacturing companies, can be very diverse, producing engineered components across more than one engineering sector. Large enterprises are those with 250 or more employees.

- Small and medium-sized engineering enterprises include companies that operate on a much smaller scale, such as small fabricators or machine shops producing engineered products for one engineering sector. SMEs have fewer than 250 employees.

All of these organisations play an important role within the engineering industry.

Large global enterprises

In today's world, with lots of progress being made in communication and transport systems, many companies find it beneficial to trade internationally. This means that they don't just sell in the same country that they are in. Some global companies employ one or two thousand people, while very large global companies may employ up to one hundred thousand people. Managing employees who are spread across the globe can be very difficult due to the different time zones and language barriers.

Moreover, many large global enterprises need to manage the **logistics** associated with manufacturing processes carried out in different countries across the world.

For example, a large organisation in the automotive sector can have:

- cars designed in Japan
- engines made in Spain
- bodywork pressed in the Far East
- gearboxes and engines made in the USA
- cars finally assembled in England – and the cars sold worldwide.

Aeroplane manufacturers are also global companies. Follow the manufacturing trail of the Airbus A380's major assemblies and components, shown in Figure 1.2 and Table 1.2, and you will see that there are significant challenges associated with the logistics of moving huge, heavy parts. This often requires specially designed transport and careful planning of traffic routes.

◘ An airbus A380

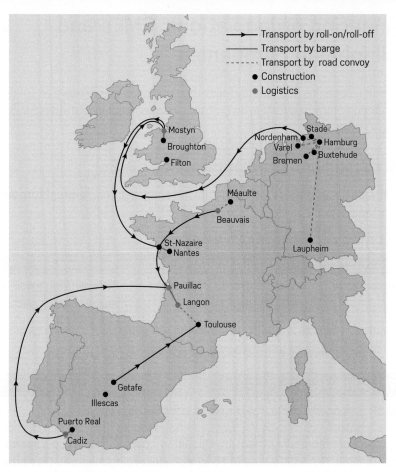

▣ Figure 1.2: Logistics trail for the Airbus A380

▣ Table 1.2: Summarised logistics trail for the Airbus A380

Component parts	Where made or assembled
Engines (gas turbines)	Made in Derby, England
Tail sections	Made in Cadiz, Spain
Wings	Made in Broughton, Wales
Fuselage sections	Made in Hamburg, Germany
Final assembly	Assembled in Toulouse, France

Not all large enterprises have logistical issues to manage in the same way as Airbus: some companies are based in a single factory that is responsible for producing all of the parts and assembling one major engineered product.

Other companies ship parts in and assemble the final product in one assembly plant. The car industry is typical of this.

ACTIVITY

Research two large international engineering companies. One could be a production/manufacturing company and the other a service company.

1 What engineered products or services do they produce or provide?

2 Where are their engineering facilities based?

3 Do they transport engineered products from factory to factory?

4 Does each factory make/supply the same or different products/services?

CHECK MY LEARNING

You should now understand when an engineering company is considered a large/global enterprise.

Carry out some online research and find three UK engineering companies that are considered large/global. How many employees do they have in the UK and worldwide?

Engineering organisations: SMEs and small jobbing companies

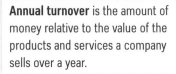
GETTING STARTED

Why do you think SMEs are important to the engineering industry? Discuss within your class.

Engineering companies that employ fewer than 250 people are known as small and medium-sized enterprises (SMEs). In fact, the accepted definition divides SMEs into three sub-categories.

Small to medium-sized enterprises (SMEs)

Each SME category has a limit on the number of employees and **annual turnover**, as shown in Table 1.3.

KEY TERM

Annual turnover is the amount of money relative to the value of the products and services a company sells over a year.

■ Table 1.3: SME categories (values from 2017)

Category	No. of employees	Annual turnover
Medium-sized	Between 50 and 249	Between £9m and £45m
Small	Between 10 and 49	Between £1.8m and £9m

The definition of an SME is actually quite important, as it allows companies in this category to access finance and support programmes.

DID YOU KNOW?

In 2017, SMEs represented 99% of all businesses in the European Union (EU).

Because there are more SMEs than large global companies, SMEs employ many more staff overall. Most SMEs tend to be independent companies and they provide engineered products across all engineering sectors. In fact, many were started up to support large companies by producing their components and parts.

Larger companies may have the advantages of more resources, greater financial backing and longer client lists, but SMEs provide greater flexibility and are often able to provide a more flexible and responsive approach because of their size.

SMEs are responsible for creating much of the innovation and competition in different engineering sectors. They can meet the demand for research or production runs more quickly than larger companies.

Small jobbing companies

KEY TERM

Customised parts are engineering products made or modified to meet the customer's specified requirements.

A small jobbing company can be one person working on their own or a company that employs up to ten people. Such companies are often started up in locations close to SMEs and large companies in order to support them by making highly specialised products or providing specialist services. These could include, for example, making one-off **customised parts** to order or engineered parts to meet the needs of a breakdown or repair order. Small jobbing companies are also very flexible and extremely used to short order lead times, sometimes turning engineered products around in less than 24 hours.

Large company vs SME

The following comparison, showing the differences between large companies and SMEs, might be useful to help you choose which kind of company you would like to work for.

◼ Table 1.4: Some of the differences between large companies and SMEs

Large/global company	SME/small jobbing company
Household-name products	Lesser/unknown products and parts
Produces standard range of engineered products – larger products, higher outputs	Produces more varied engineered products – smaller products, lower outputs
Final product may be produced on a different continent	Final product is the engineered part produced locally
Employees are generally involved in a small part of a process only – less job satisfaction	Employees are often required to work on more than one part of a process – greater job satisfaction
Multiple locations – offices and factories	Often one location
Global – different time zones	Same time zone
Red tape/bureaucracy – decisions made through many layers of management	Rapid decision-making
Bigger benefits, e.g. higher wages	Smaller benefits, e.g. lower wages
Good prospects, but harder to be noticed/ more competition	Good prospects, quicker progress, less competition, but progression might be limited

ACTIVITY

Research two SMEs in your region of the UK. One could be a production/ manufacturing company and the other a service company.

1 Where are their engineering facilities based?

2 What engineered products or services do they produce or provide?

Now answer the same questions for two small jobbing companies near your location.

CHECK MY LEARNING

You should now be familiar with the differences in size between large/global companies, SMEs and small jobbing companies.

As a group, on a wallchart, list the names and locations of the SMEs and small jobbing companies found in this lesson's activity. Using a map of the UK, place a different-coloured pin or flag for each type of company in its respective location. Is there a grouping of the small jobbing companies – are they near or far away from the SMEs? Discuss within your group.

Engineering organisations: specialist functions

There are specific functions that need to be carried out during the production of an engineered product. Many engineering organisations are set up in a similar way to perform these functions and operations – some with large teams of people, some with one person performing many job roles. While some functions may be carried out **in-house**, other functions may be subcontracted or **outsourced** to another company specialising in that particular function or operation.

Research and development (R&D) organisations

Research and development (R&D) is a very important function. However, the organisation of R&D activities may differ between companies.

KEY TERMS

In-house activities are carried out by employees of the company.
Outsourced functions are carried out by someone outside the company.

Many global/large organisations have their own internal R&D departments comprising specialist engineers and full-time researchers. In a fast-changing and developing market, R&D activities need to be carried out quickly, so companies may decide to outsource some or all or their R&D to specialist organisations that already have the resources (facilities, staff and equipment) and expertise to carry out R&D efficiently. These specialist organisations include laboratories and university departments, although university research tends to be more academic-type work.

KEY TERMS

A **patent** gives a person or company the sole right to make, sell or use a product.
The **marketplace** is a term used to describe the activities associated with the sale and purchase of a product.

The decision to outsource will depend on the commercial sensitivity of the product development and whether a product (and its **patent**) can be discussed outside the company because of **marketplace** competition or other factors.

SMEs may employ an R&D team or outsource this task, whereas small jobbing production companies rarely employ specialist staff to develop their own product. However, there are small jobbing companies that have been set up to act as small R&D companies for SMEs.

ACTIVITY

Search online for an organisation that specialises in engineering R&D. What kind of R&D do they do and who do they do it for?

Manufacturing organisations

KEY TERMS

Fabrication is the process of manufacturing something.
An **assembly line** is a process where engineers and machines assemble a product in a specified sequence.
A **machine shop** is where engineers use machine tools and cutting tools to make parts.

As with the R&D function, many organisations have their own internal manufacturing department and employ in-house engineers who convert raw materials, components or parts into finished, engineered products using **fabrication** and **assembly-line** processes. Global/large companies and some SMEs fall within this category. They include manufacturing organisations that make aircraft, motor cars or electronic devices such as cameras and mobile phones.

These products are often assembled from smaller engineered products and components that are either made in other parts of the organisation or outsourced to other companies that operate as stand-alone manufacturers. These include specialist fabrication companies and **machine shops**, which tend to be SMEs and small jobbing companies.

It is often more cost-effective to use a single assembly-line approach, sometimes using robots, than to have multiple assembly sites.

◻ **Automated car manufacture**

Service organisations

Again, many global/large engineering companies and SMEs have their own distinct departments providing customer service, also known as customer support or aftersales.

There are also independent service organisations that provide specialist services such as equipment installation and maintenance. These organisations act as a 'middle man' between the manufacturer and the customer. It is often cheaper for a manufacturing company to outsource these services than to employ permanent staff. On some engineering projects, it is the customer who employs the service organisation to look after the engineering product once it is manufactured.

For example, aerospace and airline companies work with many different service organisations. They often use specialist companies to carry out field testing and repairs to ensure that aircraft hold 'airworthiness' certificates. Engineers working in the industry need to be highly qualified and hold specific technical qualifications to work on aircraft. These qualifications limit the extent of what they can repair and sign off.

Specialist organisations in sectors

Many engineering companies can be classified as general engineering companies, using common types of equipment and engineering processes, producing the more standard types of engineered product, or working on standard contracts to supply an engineering service. In some ways, each engineering sector is specialised in its own way. They employ specialist engineers trained and qualified in their respective engineering discipline.

However, the very nature of certain engineering principles makes some engineering sectors very highly specialised. There are many engineering companies that are experts at what they do and are regarded as specialist organisations. Engineering companies involved in the manufacture of aircraft and aircraft parts, or of hydraulic and pneumatic systems, are some of the companies classified as specialist organisations.

Aircraft manufacturers

Aviation safety is critical. As a result, the aerospace sector is a safety-critical industry and aircraft part manufacturers have to work to rigorous procedures, systems and standards of testing.

One example is the manufacturers of aircraft wings. This is a highly specialised engineering area, exceptionally safety-critical to the aircraft, and is highly scientific. Aircraft wings are designed and developed to lift a specific load – that is, the aircraft and its payload (the weight of the people and cargo the aircraft is carrying) under various conditions – and aircraft wings are rigorously tested in model form within smoke tunnels and then subjected to real-load testing.

ACTIVITY

Watch some videos that show how aircraft manufacturers test their aircraft wing designs. Discuss with your group why this testing is necessary.

An aircraft is very complex, and similar constraints and testing are applied to all areas of an aircraft's design, including:

- navigation systems, which use a computer, motion sensors and rotation sensors (**gyroscopes**) to calculate the aircraft's position, **orientation** and **velocity**
- radar systems, which use radio waves to determine the position and speed of other aircraft that cannot be seen
- auxiliary power units, which produce power when the aircraft is on the ground.

These are examples of highly specialist systems of engineering, each with its own manufacturers that employ specialist engineers in the respective engineering field.

DID YOU KNOW?

Helicopter rotor systems are designed to disconnect from the engine if the engine fails during flight – the helicopter can then be landed safely using autorotation of the rotors.

KEY TERMS

Gyroscopes are wheels or discs that spin freely on their axes to find their orientation by themselves.

The **orientation** of an object is its direction or relative position.

Velocity is an object's direction and speed of movement.

Manufacturers of hydraulic and pneumatic systems

Companies that develop hydraulic and pneumatic systems and circuits similarly need specialist engineers to meet the challenges of engineering these systems. Very few people are aware of the use and significance of hydraulics or pneumatics in their everyday lives, even though they are surrounded by these systems all the time.

Both hydraulic and pneumatic systems use **fluid** pressure to move internal components, such as a piston within a cylinder, to operate machinery or lift objects.

- **Hydraulic systems** use oil in their circuits. Oil is **non-compressible**, and hydraulic systems are used to lift heavy loads.
- **Pneumatic systems** use air in their circuits. Air is **compressible** and is used for lifting lighter loads.

When you open the doors of a train or bus, they are normally powered by either hydraulic or pneumatic systems. There are also many hydraulic systems in an aircraft. Without them, the landing gear would neither retract after take-off nor be deployed for landing.

Figure 1.3 shows how a car jack is operated by hydraulics.

KEY TERMS

A **fluid** is a gas or liquid.
Non-compressible means that a fluid cannot be compressed.
Compressible is when the volume of a fluid can change when pressure is applied to it.

■ A car jack

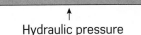

Hydraulic pressure

■ Figure 1.3: A simple hydraulic system to operate a car jack

ACTIVITY

1 Research the following online to find out what they are.
   a) Auxiliary power unit   b) Radar system
2 Find out what hydraulic systems are used in motor vehicles and the names of organisations involved. Make some notes to help explain how these systems work.

CHECK MY LEARNING

You have been introduced to the roles of specialist organisations.

Explain why there are specialist organisations in some engineering sectors. Write down your answer, using a specific example to back up your explanation.

Functions in engineering organisations

GETTING STARTED

Can you think of other functions that are required in engineering organisations? Discuss and compare your ideas with a partner.

Engineering organisations perform a range of functions to manage their businesses. Good communication between functions is essential, otherwise the end result could be very different from what was expected (see, for example, Figure 1.4)!

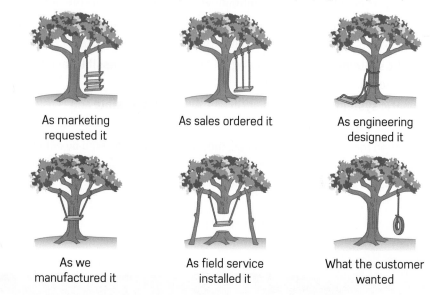

| As marketing requested it | As sales ordered it | As engineering designed it |
| As we manufactured it | As field service installed it | What the customer wanted |

◘ **Figure 1.4: What did the customer order?**

Research and development (R&D)

R&D is carried out to improve existing products or develop ideas for new products. This is done at an early stage in the 'innovation life cycle', which is a process used to confirm whether there is value in bringing an innovation into the marketplace (see Figure 1.5). Many R&D teams need to act quickly to maintain a lead in a fast-changing and developing market.

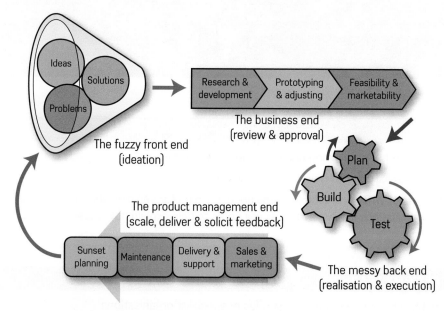

◘ **Figure 1.5: The innovation life cycle**

When developing new products, specialist engineers will:

- research new materials
- make items more economical
- solve assembly problems
- make modifications to an existing product.

A product idea may go through many hours of research and development, including the design, build and testing of a concept or prototype, before the idea is released for manufacturing design to begin.

Design

Engineering design starts with several sketches of what the final product may look like (see, for example, Figure 1.6). Models are also often constructed to help visualise any problems.

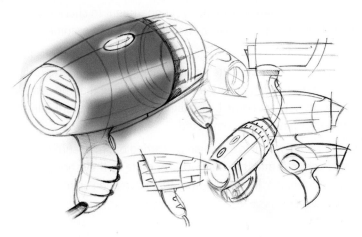

◾ **Figure 1.6: Design sketch**

Designers need to consider many details, including – all of the information required to manufacture a product. This includes knowing what is already available on the market, what the engineered product is to be used for, and the materials and engineering production methods that will be used in the product's manufacture. The product's design needs to be fit for purpose, last for its intended lifetime and be safe to use.

Planning

Once the design has been finalised, a plan needs to be developed so that the engineered product can be made in a timely, cost-effective and safe manner. Planning engineers interpret the product design and turn it into a production plan, which contains:

- the required materials that need to be purchased
- tooling and equipment that need to be allocated
- work instructions and health and safety requirements that need to be issued.

Making

Making is the process step associated with the manufacture of an engineered product. Production operatives need to follow the planning instructions carefully and safely, ensuring they have the correct materials and that tooling and equipment is set up and used correctly, to produce an engineered product that meets the requirements of the design.

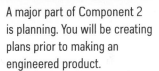

LINK IT UP

A major part of Component 2 is planning. You will be creating plans prior to making an engineered product.

ACTIVITY

With a partner, create a flow chart on a large sheet of paper. List the four engineering functions covered in this lesson, leaving a reasonable space between them. Draw a circle around each function. Now draw arrows between the circles showing the process steps normally adopted in engineering organisations. Next to each arrow, jot down some notes to explain what it represents, that is, the activities at each step.

LINK IT UP

Go to the making section in Component 2 for a description of the making process and materials.

CHECK MY LEARNING

You have learned about four of the functions in an engineering organisation. Now discuss within your class.

Functions in engineering organisations

Making an engineered product is not the end of the process. There are additional important functions that ensure the final engineered product is:

- fit for purpose and meets the customer's expectations
- installed and commissioned correctly
- supported, by way of servicing or information, throughout its lifetime of use
- advertised to increase sales.

Quality

When engineered products are made, it is essential that they **conform** to the design and are suitable for their intended purpose. Companies may have a **quality assurance** (QA) and/or **quality control** (QC) department to check product quality – that it conforms, has no faults and will be acceptable to the customer.

Many companies will have a QA/QC system, where regular inspections and quality checks are carried out throughout the production of an engineered product. Quality engineers carry out monitoring at various stages, checking that the correct drawings are being used, materials are correct, and dimensions are accurate during and after production processes have been completed.

Factory testing of some products may also be carried out to ensure that they have been assembled correctly and that they work/operate as they should, meeting any predetermined performance levels of output that have been specified, designed and agreed by the customer.

Marketing

Marketing departments and companies are involved with promoting and selling products and services. This includes carrying out market research and advertising the product, plus any **branding** that will help to promote the company and its products.

Some companies will have internal marketing departments; some will outsource this function to an external marketing company. Much will depend on the sensitivity of product information and the amount of marketing required.

Selling

The selling (or sales) function is performed by a company's sales department, although sales and marketing departments often work closely together. The product being sold might be a standard 'stock' engineered product or, alternatively, a bespoke design solution associated with site equipment installation projects.

Many organisations will have internal and/or external sales engineers whose responsibility is to interact and build connections with customers and improve the sales of products and services within the business. Persons from other functions may be involved in the selling process to help promote the overall effectiveness of an organisation.

Customer service

A customer service department provides support to customers who have bought or use a company's products or services. This includes telephone support offering advice and information, preventative maintenance associated with routine servicing, and carrying out equipment repairs when required. The specialist nature of some equipment maintenance and repairs means that the company is often the best option, especially when the product and equipment are still under **warranty**.

◘ **Hydraulic servicing**

Installation

The complexity of certain engineered products and equipment means that installation, if required, is best carried out by trained engineers with specialist knowledge of the product. Engineering companies may have an installation department or they may choose to outsource this function to another company that also has the specialist know-how.

Equipment installation can also include commissioning and testing activities, and so may involve several different engineers with different skills.

CHECK MY LEARNING ■ ■

You have covered five more functions in an engineering organisation. Discuss within your class.

As a homework task, research information online and create a table, listing all nine functions from both lessons, and then identify those that a global/large organisation, SME and small jobbing company might employ.

ACTIVITY

With the same partner and the flow chart you started in the previous lesson, add the five functions covered in this lesson. Complete the chart by adding arrows between the process steps. Once again, add notes to explain what each arrow represents, that is, the activities at each step.

Engineering job roles 1

Engineering organisations employ many different people with a variety of skills. All are important, from the person who makes an engineered product to the person who services and repairs the product once it has been installed, for example, in a production factory.

Maintenance technician

Engineering maintenance technicians service and repair mechanical and electrical equipment and systems used in the engineering industry. The maintenance could be either preventative, where it is planned and carried out to a routine service schedule, or in response to an emergency involving equipment breakdown.

Routine servicing includes carrying out:

- periodic inspection checks of equipment (daily, weekly, monthly, etc.), looking to see if there are any oil or water leaks and listening for any unusual noises coming from the equipment
- regular activities that keep equipment running well, e.g. changing the oil in hydraulic systems, greasing motor bearings, or replacing consumable parts such as filters.

In an emergency, a maintenance technician could be the first person on the scene on a breakdown. They will need to use **troubleshooting** skills to repair the equipment and get it working as soon as possible, particularly if the equipment is part of an important production line or manufacturing process.

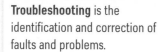

KEY TERMS

Troubleshooting is the identification and correction of faults and problems.

Machine operator

Machine operators operate machinery, such as drills and lathes, that is used in the production of engineered product parts and components. This includes computer numerical control (CNC) machines.

Machine operators follow a production plan that tells them the batch quantities required of the product, any equipment needed, inspection checks that need to be carried out, and any safety requirements. The operators are responsible for loading and unloading the material onto the machine, and ensuring a CNC machine is correctly programmed, the correct tooling is being used, and the finished quality of the machined component is acceptable.

Some machine operators check the product as it is being machined. Some CNC machines have built-in checks and adjust the tooling if the product is undersized or oversized. Some machine operators change the tooling on the machine at pre-set intervals. Some CNC machines have tooling that changes automatically.

◘ Machine operator

Aircraft fitter

Aircraft fitters are employed in both aircraft manufacturing and aircraft maintenance. Their roles may include various activities during assembly, such as in the build of wings and the fuselage, and carrying out structural repairs on old or damaged parts, such as on the wings or in the flooring and doors.

Aircraft fitters need to be skilled in sheet metal work and in the use of precision tools for drilling, bolting and riveting. They also need to have a broad knowledge of an aircraft's engines and its mechanical and electrical systems, and of the **composite materials** that are commonly used in modern aircraft.

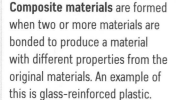

KEY TERM

Composite materials are formed when two or more materials are bonded to produce a material with different properties from the original materials. An example of this is glass-reinforced plastic.

■ Aircraft fitter mounting fan blades

DID YOU KNOW?

Glass-reinforced plastic (GRP), or fibreglass, is a typical composite made by reinforcing plastic with fine glass fibres.

LINK IT UP

To find out more about the categories, properties and characteristics of materials, go to Component 2.

Design engineer

Design engineers develop an initial idea for a product by using their knowledge of scientific principles, undertaking mathematical calculations, and producing sketches and engineering drawings. Many use computer-aided design (CAD) packages to create 2D/3D drawings and use complex software to evaluate and solve problems. Product testing can now be conducted using **virtual reality** and prototypes created with 3D printers.

KEY TERMS

Virtual reality is a computer technology that uses special equipment such as headsets to create images, sounds and other sensations that simulate a user's physical presence in a virtual or imaginary environment.

ACTIVITY

Research the four job roles in this lesson and the skills required for each, and make notes. With your partner, discuss your notes and then create a poster that could be used to advertise vacancies for one of the job roles. Present it to your class.

CHECK MY LEARNING

Using the research notes you made during the class activity, create a mind map to include all the job roles you have learned about. Add information on skills required for each role. Are there any similarities between job roles? Discuss with your class group.

Engineering job roles 2

This lesson provides further information on other job roles that engineering organisations need to run their businesses successfully.

Manufacturing engineer

Manufacturing engineers use their engineering skills and knowledge to improve manufacturing processes, ensuring that a product can be manufactured efficiently and safely, and that the final engineered product can be made cost-effectively.

Manufacturing engineers are heavily involved in both the design of new production lines and the modification and improvement of existing processes. Their job roles include:

- assessing and developing manufacturing processes, using their knowledge of product design, materials, tooling, and fabrication and assembly methods
- improving the efficiency of working methods by carefully looking at:
  - how well work flows from one process to the next
  - the way production workspace is used and the best equipment layout
  - scheduling of the best times to carry out equipment maintenance
- designing test methods so that the highest product quality is achieved
- monitoring processes, checking software and making changes where necessary.

To ensure complete cost-effectiveness, many manufacturing engineers are involved in negotiating the purchase costs for machinery and manufacturing equipment.

Installation engineer

KEY TERMS

Ancillary equipment covers any items of equipment required by the main equipment system to be a complete system.
Commissioning is the final testing and verification of the equipment's functionality.
Handover means that possession of the equipment is passed to the customer.

Installation engineer is quite a broad term, but generally refers to those who travel to the customer's premises to install the main equipment system and connect any **ancillary equipment**. Ultimately, they are involved with:

- equipment delivery
- positioning and fixing the equipment on site
- preparing and **commissioning** the equipment
- obtaining the customer's acceptance/**handover**.

Installation engineers may be trained more in mechanical or electrical engineering. However, many installation engineers are now also multi-disciplined because of the complexities of newer products, which may need more than one engineering discipline to create them. For example, installation engineers are often involved with air conditioning systems; security and information technology systems, including cabling and fibre optics; communications equipment systems; mechanical machinery and equipment; and assembly-line equipment systems.

Process engineer

Process engineers work in companies that have a continuous process operation, such as in oil refineries, which have very complex, critical refining processes, operating twenty-four hours a day, seven days a week and, making allowance for any planned maintenance, 365 days a year. A process engineer's job role includes:

- developing and organising the industrial processes – planning pipe routes, positioning **control valves**
- monitoring and analysing process data – checking system pressures and control **setpoints**
- designing system upgrades to improve outputs – upgrading software.

Telecommunications engineer

Telecommunications engineers use their electrical and electronics knowledge to look after communications technology, such as landline and wireless telephone networks, internet and broadband technologies, fibre optic networks, and radio and satellite communications systems.

Working for telecoms service providers, engineers are involved with the design, development and setting up of communications and data networks. This includes the installation of underground cabling, testing system equipment, and finding and fixing system faults.

◩ **Installation and telecommunications engineer**

KEY TERMS

Control valves are automatic devices used to control fluids in a pipe.

Setpoints are target values for a process value, e.g. maximum temperature, minimum flow rate.

CHECK MY LEARNING

Update the mind map from the previous lesson to include the four job roles you have learned about in this lesson, adding information on the skills required for each role.

Are there any similarities between the job roles? Which industry sectors do you think a manufacturing engineer could work in? Discuss with your class group.

ACTIVITY

Carry out further research into each of the four job roles in this lesson and the skills required for them, and make notes. Discuss with your partner.

At the start of the previous lesson, you were asked how many different job roles you could think of. Compare your original list with the eight job roles covered in both lessons. Discuss any different job roles you have identified with your class group.

Career progression opportunities

GETTING STARTED

Which engineering sector, organisation function or job role interests you the most so far and why? Write some notes on the reasons for your choice(s). This will be useful when you come to make a decision in the future. (Table 1.4 on page 17 had some useful points.)

ACTIVITY

With a partner, research online advertisements for an engineering job. Make notes on the qualifications, training and experience required for this job. Does the job also offer any training or qualifications? Discuss with your partner.

Choosing the right job is a very important decision. There might be one particular choice that is attractive right now. However, you also need to think about opportunities that will allow your career to progress.

A structured career path is important, as in any industry, and is available and accessible within the engineering industry. Many managing directors have started as apprentices and then worked their way up to various positions within the boardroom.

The following are some of the levels you could follow along your career path.

Apprentice

An apprentice is a person who learns from on-the-job training with a skilled employer over a set period of time. Many engineering sectors offer apprenticeships, including in manufacturing, and in mechanical, electrical and aerospace engineering. Time will probably be spent at college to learn the theory side of the job.

Apprentices normally begin by being shown simple tasks and performing these under supervision, before moving on to more complex tasks.

Apprenticeships have no upper age limits and are not limited to school-leavers.

■ Engineering apprentice under instruction

DID YOU KNOW?

The first national apprenticeship system in England was introduced during the 16th century.

Operator

An operator can be trained as an apprentice to an intermediate standard to **NVQ** Level 2 with supporting academic qualifications, which are together the vocational equivalent of five GCSEs at grade 4 or above. A trained operator can then probably follow a career as a machine operator.

Technician

A technician will start their training from an intermediate apprenticeship standard and progress to NVQ Level 3 with supporting academic qualifications, which are together the vocational equivalent of two A level passes required for an advanced apprenticeship.

Technical

A future technical engineer will start their training from an advanced apprenticeship standard and progress to NVQ Level 4/5 with supporting academic qualifications such as a Higher National Certificate (HNC) or a Higher National Diploma (HND). Together, these are the vocational qualifications required to progress to a university qualification.

Professional

A professional engineer can start their training from a higher apprenticeship standard and progress to degree-level academic qualifications at university, possibly leading to **chartered engineer** status.

Management

There are two routes into management:

1 It is perfectly possible to start a job with an apprenticeship scheme and progress through promotion to become a junior supervisor and then move on to a management position.

2 Alternatively, a career path can be followed via a structured management training scheme, progressing from a higher apprenticeship standard to a degree-level academic qualification, before working towards promotion to junior and then senior management roles.

KEY TERMS

NVQ stands for National Vocational Qualification: a practical qualification gained through employment.

A **chartered engineer** is registered with the Engineering Council as a person who has academic qualifications, technical training and knowledge, and practical experience. They are permitted to use the abbreviation CEng after their name.

ACTIVITY

With your partner, search online for engineering jobs advertised by a global/large organisation, SME and small jobbing company – one job for each type of company. Make notes on the qualifications, training and experience required for these jobs. Is there mention of any on-the-job training or opportunities to gain further qualifications? Discuss with your class group.

CHECK MY LEARNING

You have now seen some of the different routes into the engineering industry.

With the same partner, compare the notes you made at the start of the lesson with those you made during the lesson. Have you changed your mind? Discuss with your teacher.

Role definitions

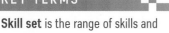

Have you heard the terms skilled and unskilled? Do you know what these terms mean?

KEY TERMS

Skill set is the range of skills and abilities that a person has.
A **chargehand** is a worker put in charge of others.

Engineering organisations employ a variety of people to perform jobs within their various functions. Larger organisations require greater numbers of employees and often have a greater variety of job roles and required skills. Smaller organisations employ fewer people and usually need a smaller variety of job roles – although some people are employed to cover more than one role and may therefore be required to have a broader **skill set**. No matter what the size of the organisation, all these people have important roles to play.

Employee job roles are generally defined as belonging to one of four skill categories. These categories are:

- unskilled
- skilled
- technical
- managerial.

Unlike some industries and trades that limit career progression, with additional training and qualifications it is possible to progress your career in engineering from an unskilled to a managerial role.

Unskilled

Unskilled employees work in job roles that require no, or very few, skills and training, and that require minimum experience. Job roles include tasks that are repetitive and can be learned easily and quickly. Unskilled employees have few, if any, responsibilities and are usually supervised in a small team by a junior supervisor or **chargehand**.

Some assembly-line production work falls within this category – for example, where the task is a very simple process of fitting engineering parts together. However, an unskilled employee can gain the experience and training necessary to become a machine operator.

Skilled

Skilled employees work in job roles that require some specialist skills and training and a certain level of experience so that tasks can be completed successfully. There are also low-skilled and semi-skilled employees who carry out job roles that require a basic level of knowledge, training and/or experience.

In an engineering company, skilled employees might work in a workshop, using machine tools and carrying out highly skilled and intricate work. They may also work alone, visiting customers' premises to install equipment and systems – for example, installing cabling or fibre optics, and connecting satellite communications systems.

This category also includes multi-skilled engineers, such as maintenance engineers who deal with both mechanical and electrical equipment systems.

Technical

Technical engineering employees are trained and qualified to work in a technical position in which they perform various job roles in departments such as R&D, design and quality control.

Technical employees have a greater level of responsibility, for example, producing essential information for the company's engineering processes. A manufacturing engineer is an example, where the work includes planning the details for machine tool settings, material and resource planning, monitoring and measuring process data and efficiency, and ensuring that the engineered product meets the stringent requirements of quality control.

Technical employees are usually managed by the department manager, who will have overall responsibility for allocating work schedules and activities.

◘ **Technician/technical engineers and manager developing new engineered products**

Managerial

Managerial employees are often qualified to degree level. They may well have served an apprenticeship, following a career path through skilled and technical roles and then on to junior and senior managerial positions.

Managers are those individuals with final responsibility for the control and administration of the activities carried out and for the employees working within the respective functional department. As part of the company's management team, they often report directly to the company's directors.

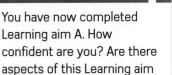

ACTIVITY

In the last few lessons, you have explored job roles and role definitions as well as career progression opportunities.

1 Research a global/large engineering company and create a table listing the various job roles you think they require. Against each job role, define whether it is unskilled, skilled, technical or managerial. Discuss with a partner.

2 Using the notes you made in the lesson on career progression, plot a simple flow chart of the job roles you think you would need to perform to work your way up from apprentice to managing director of a global/large engineering company. Discuss with your class group.

CHECK MY LEARNING

You have now completed Learning aim A. How confident are you? Are there aspects of this Learning aim that you need to revise? List the topics you understand and those you need to find out more about, and revise the ones you feel less confident with.

Learning aim A: assessment practice

How you will be assessed

In Component 1 you will be assessed by completing a series of internally set assignments.

When completing the assignment covering Learning Aim A, you will need to show that you understand how a range of engineering sectors, products and organisations relate to one another.

This will include demonstrating a detailed understanding of:

- how engineering sectors and engineered products are interconnected
- how engineering companies of varying sizes operate, and the functions they carry out
- the job roles available in different sectors, and typical career pathways.

CHECKPOINT

Strengthen

- Ensure you can recognise the different engineering sectors. List as many as you can, and suggest typical examples of what each one manufactures.
- Identify and describe different job roles in a range of engineering organisations.
- Identify the sectors involved in the design and manufacture of a range of engineering products.

Challenge

- Research engineering jobs currently available in engineering organisations near you and analyse the qualifications, skills and experience required to carry them out.
- Justify why engineering organisations from different sectors need to cooperate when designing and building complex engineered products (e.g. car, aircraft). Consider the sizes of organisations, their key functions and the job roles involved.

TIPS

Written evidence should be broken down into different sections using clear sub headings. This will keep your work well organised, easy to read and easy for you to check that all the different parts of the task have been covered.

ASSESSMENT ACTIVITY   LEARNING AIM   **A**

Description

In this assignment you will be asked to carry out research into engineering sectors, products and organisations, and how they all interrelate.

Example tasks

Select an engineered product from the following list.

- Hairdryer.
- Computer keyboard.
- Bicycle.
- Kettle.
- Motorbike.

Then, complete the following tasks on your chosen engineered product.

1 Research the different engineering sectors in which two of the major components/assemblies of the engineered product have been manufactured.
2 Identify the links between the sectors.
3 Make detailed notes on the sectors and how they combine to make the two major components/assemblies of the engineered product.

Now you have identified the different sectors, identify one named organisation from each of the sectors. The organisations you choose should be of different sizes. Then carry out Internet research to find out:

- how many people each organisation employs
- how each is organised, e.g. is it single site in the UK or does it have manufacturing facilities in different countries
- the different departments in each organisation and the links between them
- the job roles and career progression opportunities within each organisation.

You need to gather all of your findings into a small folder, which will help to organise and present your evidence. The small folder must include a detailed commentary on why:

- the engineered product is made collaboratively by different organisations of different sizes
- specialist engineering organisations from different sectors are needed when producing the complex engineered product
- engineers from different sectors cooperate to produce the engineered product that contains numerous major components/assemblies that link together
- certain job roles are required in the different organisations when producing a complex engineered product, so that activities can be carried out at the correct time and in the correct manner, and the skills of those involved are best utilised.

Evidence

Suggested evidence includes:

- researched information
- detailed written commentary
- block diagrams showing interconnectivity and flow charts/images (all to support the written commentary).

TAKE IT FURTHER

Analyse a complex engineered product and identify all the sectors that are involved in its design and manufacture. Explain the role of the engineering organisations within each sector and the functions that they provide.

The engineering design and make process

GETTING STARTED

There are five main steps in the engineering design and make process. Can you identify what these steps are called?

The development and creation of new engineered products (including making any improvements to existing products) requires logical manufacturing processes to ensure the product can be made as easily and quickly as possible, and at the optimum manufacturing cost.

Getting the product right is essential. Interpreting and understanding what exactly the product is for and how it should be used is critical right from the start of the process.

Using different combinations of engineering skills, including starting with good engineering design and applying a five-step design process (see Figure 1.7) helps to achieve the desired results.

1. Define the problem

The first and probably the most important step of a design project is to define clearly what the engineering problem is. In practice, this means being able to answer the following questions:

- What is the engineered product and what is it meant to do?
- Who is the product for? How/where will it be used?
- Has it been done before and, if so, how – can an existing solution be reused?
- Are there any limitations, including specific customer requirements, e.g. types of material, costs, time to complete?

2. Develop possible solutions

The second step is to develop possible ideas and solutions:

- **Brainstorm**, seeking ideas from others – come up with as many solutions as possible.
- This is often an **iterative** process – work through each solution to see if it is feasible.
- Be innovative – discard solutions only when you are sure there are better solutions.

KEY TERMS

Brainstorming is an open group discussion of ideas to find solutions.
Iteration means repeating a process until the best solution is identified.

3. Choose a solution

Step three is to select the best solution that you have come up with:

- Analyse and compare each solution using a list of criteria, e.g. materials required, estimates of costs involved and of manufacturing time.
- Does the best solution meet the customer's requirements?

4. Design and model the solution

Step four is to take the solution, turn it into a design and create a model:

- Produce design sketches and drawings, including lists of materials and equipment needed to make it.
- If any problems are envisaged during the design process, make the necessary changes. Compare against the design the needs of the design brief.
- Manufacture a model of the proposed product, again making changes if necessary.

5. Evaluate the outcome

The final step in this process is to evaluate the solution:

- Carry out some product testing – check the product against the initial problem definition: does it look like and do what the customer wanted?
- If not, why not? What needs to be changed?
- Are there any further improvements that can be made to make the product more efficient and cost-effective to manufacture?

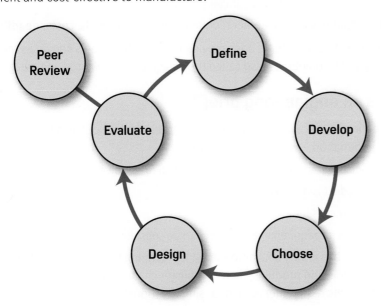

LINK IT UP

Go to Component 2, page 120 to find out more about the engineering make process.

◘ Figure 1.7: The five steps of the engineering design and make process

Work in a team

Designers very rarely work on projects by themselves. Most products are created by teamwork, requiring specialist input from engineers from various disciplines to analyse ideas and review and suggest improvements.

ACTIVITY

Working in small teams, identify an idea for an engineered product and work through the five steps of the engineering design process, making notes as you go. For example, you might help your local council to create or redesign a device to crush plastic bottles before they are put into household recycling bins.

Present your idea and the results from the five-step process to your class group.

CHECK MY LEARNING

You have looked at the engineering design and make process and learned about its five steps.

Think of an innovative idea for a new product (perhaps an idea you have come up with in previous lessons) or for an existing product that could be improved.

Work through the five steps for your idea and consider what you would need to do. What do you think now? Do you see any problems you had not originally thought about?

The engineering brief

In the previous lesson on the engineering design and make process, you were introduced to the five-step process. The first step was to 'define the problem', in this case defining an engineered product as the problem, which includes considering:

- the function of the engineered product
- the customer or people who will use the product
- whether there is an existing or similar product
- specific limitations and customer requirements, e.g. materials, costs, **deadlines**.

This list is not exhaustive, but it does provide the basis for what is known as the engineering brief, sometimes also called the design brief or engineering design brief.

What is an engineering brief?

An engineering brief is a written document or statement that outlines the following essential information – **what**, **why** and **who**.

1 **What** product is to be made (what is the problem to be solved?)

2 **Why** the product is required.

3 **Who** the product is for.

4 Any other specific requirements also need to be considered.

As you can see, this is very similar to the list for 'defining the problem'. With more complex problems and products, there is a bigger chance that there will be a greater number of specific requirements than for simple products.

As the engineering brief is starting to be written, however, remain open-minded and do not confirm a solution just yet. The development of the final solution will come later in the design process.

Interpreting customer requirements

An engineering brief is generally written in response to a customer's enquiry or technical specification – a list of their detailed requirements. The customer's information might just be a simple idea or concept, or it might be a full specification document listing the requirements over many pages.

The customer might be an external company that requires a new product to be designed or they could be an internal customer, e.g. a sales department that needs an existing product range to be expanded or improved.

The customer's requirements will need to be reviewed and interpreted carefully to establish the essential information that needs to be listed in the engineering brief. Many companies use the engineering brief to confirm that they have fully understood the customer's requirements by issuing it to the customer for their approval and, where necessary, holding a meeting with the customer to discuss and review the brief. The same can also apply to internal 'customers'.

Example engineering brief

A supplier of camping equipment believes there is a market for a portable, lightweight wind-powered device that could provide enough energy to operate a small camping lamp. (The supplier has already considered a solar-powered option and found it was not viable.)

From this simple statement, the writer of the engineering brief needs to think about **what**, **why**, **who**, and any other specific requirements. The following is an example of an initial outline engineering brief.

Engineering brief for a portable wind-powered device

Design statement: To design and make a wind-powered device to power a small camping lamp

Customer name: Adventure Camping

Today's date: January 3rd

Design review date: Feb 28th

Due date for completion: end of May (in time for the holiday season)

Cost/budget: £5 maximum

Product: Wind turbine to power a camping lamp DC bulb

Target end users: Campers, mountaineers, walkers, hobbyists

List of everything this project is expected to deliver:

- Low-level light when there is no external power or no batteries available
- To work in a low-wind source
- Pack flat, ease of assembly, quickly assembled
- Portable, small
- The device must be able to generate sufficient DC electricity to light a small light bulb or light-emitting diode (LED). If I use an LED the circuit will be more complex.

This example is a very simple brief, whereas complex briefs could extend over many pages. Whatever the complexity, the engineering brief is a written record that can be used to check that the customer's requirements have been met, and the brief is updated if any changes to the original requirements are subsequently made.

ACTIVITY

Your local authority has approached the company you work for. They want a simple-to-use, lightweight and strong device that will help teach young schoolchildren how to add and subtract simple numbers. The product must be inexpensive (less than £5 per unit to make), and it is needed for the start of the school term. Working with your partner and using the example above as an outline, create an engineering brief that contains all of the required details.

CHECK MY LEARNING

You have now started to look at an engineering brief. These can often be developed with much greater detail.

Once again, think of the innovative product idea you had in previous lessons, and now write a simple engineering brief. Swap with a partner, and write a brief summary of what you have read, interpreting the brief as best you can.

Criteria for an engineering brief

In terms of the amount of information and the size of the document, engineering briefs can vary enormously. An outline of a short, simple engineering brief was covered in the previous lesson. However, as you might expect, an engineering brief for complex equipment products and systems will typically need a much deeper analysis to fully understand the customer's specific requirements.

Essential information must not be missed off an engineering brief. This information must be accurate. One way to ensure this is to check standard, specific factors each time an engineering brief needs to be developed. Such factors include:

- physical requirements
- aesthetics
- size
- function
- performance requirements.

The information for each of these factors will vary for different products. However, these five factors provide a good starting point and a good checklist to work to.

Physical requirements

This covers many areas, including:

- Is the product to be used in connection with other equipment or systems?
- Will it be subject to any loading, that is, will it need to support or move a known weight?
- Could the materials the product is made of be affected by environmental conditions, e.g. ambient temperature, humidity, noise, vibration, lighting, ground conditions?

Aesthetics

The appearance of a product could be one of the most important factors to many customers. The product may need to possess the following characteristics:

- have a good shape and appearance, and look strong and robust where it needs to be
- be easy to use and have a compact form
- have the correct material finish, e.g. polished, shiny chrome finish or painted finish to the correct colour.

Size

The size and quantity of the product also matter:

- How many of the product are required, e.g. is it a special one-off design?
- Is there a required size: not too small, not too big? Consider the dimensions associated with height, width and length, and any dimensional **tolerances**.
- Are there any weight restrictions when considering how and where it will be used?
- Is it replacing existing equipment, the size of which might restrict the size of the new equipment?

Function

This will usually be quite a detailed section in the engineering brief, and some of the criteria may overlap with the performance requirements:

- What does the product need to do?
- Consider **ergonomics**: is the product easy to operate and maintain?
- Is the product safe, not just for the operator but for the public and the environment?

Performance requirements

This will eventually be used to measure how successful the product is and will include the minimum performance levels it must achieve. For example:

- At what speeds should product equipment operate?
- Is the product economic to manufacture, purchase and operate in the long term?
- Is there a specified lifetime for the product?
- Is regular maintenance of the equipment required?

The list of criteria is extensive, and there are too many points to cover here. Hopefully, though, this provides an insight into the type of information that needs to be considered in the brief for an engineered product.

The engineering brief should provide a breakdown of the information the designer needs to think about. If it appears that something is unclear or confusing, or information is missing, do not hesitate to contact the customer and clarify any points.

ACTIVITY

With a partner, design a pro forma sheet for a typical engineering brief. A pro forma sheet is used to predict the future state of a company's health. Start with a title section, where the project description, date, design statement, etc. can be inserted, and then make a section for the five factors, listing what you think are standard questions in relation to each.

CHECK MY LEARNING

Using the pro forma engineering brief you have developed, redo the example brief for the portable wind-powered device in the previous lesson, populating the brief with more information than the simple brief contained. Discuss with your partner whether the information is now more complete.

Interpreting an engineering brief

KEY TERM

Interpretation is an opinion of what something means; when you interpret something, you are deciding what you believe to be the meaning.

Your involvement with **interpreting** an engineering brief may vary depending on 'which side of the table' you are sitting at – your position and responsibilities within the engineering design process.

- Are you the person in the company who is responsible for interpreting and creating the engineering brief from the original information provided by the customer?
- Are you the customer who sent the original information, and who now wishes to ensure the information has been correctly interpreted in the engineering brief?
- Are you another company person who has to interpret the engineering brief at a later stage and, consequently, implement further actions associated with design and manufacturing processes?

Do you see any links within and between the above points? There is, of course, the relationship between the customer and the company. There is also 'the engineering brief' and the issue of 'interpretation'.

ACTIVITY

You work for an engineering company that manufactures plastic components and parts. As the person who deals with producing engineering design briefs for all orders, you receive the following email from sales, who have received an order from a regular, important customer that makes model toys:

'They require a range lightweight plastic wheels with black tyres, a range of three different sizes (25mm, 50mm, 100mm dia.), 100 of each, for their toy dumper trucks, by tomorrow. Thanks.'

It's 4.40 p.m. and you know that, to have any chance of meeting the deadline for delivery, production of the plastic wheels will have to be started during tonight's night shift. You have 20 minutes to produce the engineering brief, so you need to work fast. Think about the factors that were covered in the previous lessons.

The product is quite straightforward, so it looks like a simple brief should do. And it doesn't need a special drawing to be produced, as this customer always has a standard wheel design.

When you're finished, work in small teams of three and discuss, with each person in the team acting as:

- the engineering brief creator
- the customer
- the operator of the production machinery that makes the wheels.

◘ **Toy dumper truck**

Understanding the engineering brief

The engineering brief creator

Some briefs will be simple and straightforward, and others more complex. Experience may help you to decide into which category a customer requirement falls, especially when the job is urgent and there is not much time.

However, this can be dangerous. It is very easy to overlook something, miss an important piece of information, or rush something and make an error. It is always best to check thoroughly, using a checklist so you can be sure you've covered all of the essential factors.

If you had double-checked, you would have been told that the customer required 'orange lightweight plastic wheels' – a very simple example of a typo, in this case, but this sort of thing happens!

The customer

It might not have been clear what colour the wheels should be. Did the customer's original order specify the colour of the wheels, or was the typo made in the email from sales?

For this very reason of interpretation, many companies prescribe the mandatory process step of issuing important documentation to the customer for their approval – a double-check, to ensure the customer's requirements have been correctly interpreted and fully understood. Many customers also now expect to receive confirmation of their requirements when they receive an order acknowledgement.

The engineering brief receiver

When an urgent order comes through, the company will be pushing to honour the customer's deadline – often a case of 'full steam ahead'.

As the person receiving what you believe to be a correct engineering brief, that is what you work to. You may be the production operator or, more typically, the design engineer who will continue and perhaps complete the product design.

With an appreciation of what goes into an engineering brief and knowing about the various factors that should be covered in the brief, experience should make you aware of when important details are missing or need to be checked.

> **DID YOU KNOW?**
>
> Document approval is a very important requirement of ISO 9000 – a quality management standard that provides guidelines for businesses. Look it up online.

ACTIVITY

Consider a small engineered product that you want to buy, e.g. a mobile phone. Write a specification with a list of features and functions you want the product to have.

Swap the specification with a partner and then each of you create an engineering brief based on the exact requirements in the specification you have received. When finished, discuss with your partner.

CHECK MY LEARNING

You have had a quick introduction to engineering briefs. Talk to a friend or family member who has recently purchased a large product, such as a car, TV or laptop. Did they receive a specification with the features and functions of the product – a document listing exactly what they had ordered?

Organising your design folder

The design of an engineered product, from its initial proposal to its final design solution, should be organised. Discuss with a partner why you think this is.

■ Now where did I put that calculation sheet?

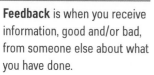

KEY TERM

Feedback is when you receive information, good and/or bad, from someone else about what you have done.
Iterative means repeating a process many times to make something better.

Design is an iterative process. All designers use iteration. They create an initial design and then, through various stages of review and **feedback** from others involved in the process, including customers and other designers, they improve the design.

This **iterative** approach to design work means that it is essential that the overall process is controlled and managed in a systematic and logical way. Improvements need to be made at each stage. These improvements need to be made in a logical way.

In addition to being unable to find information quickly when you want it, if the design process is not well organised and carefully managed, confusion can easily arise, especially if any design changes are not documented correctly. This can be costly to a company if design errors are incurred, which may also lead to safety concerns over the final product design.

It is considered good engineering practice to construct a design file for every product design. In fact, many engineering companies have a set structure for their design files.

Keep all information in a design folder

Records should be kept of all notes, sketches, drawings, calculations and photographs. These are normally filed away in the product or project design file, as both hard copy and computer files.

Remember the five steps in the engineering design and make process. These make good section headings for the structure of the design file. Each section can then be organised into subsections according to the information it contains, e.g. material data, calculation sheets. Strictly speaking, you don't have to use these titles – they can be adjusted to suit the product. As you gain experience, you will be able to tell straight away the best structure for each product design.

Table 1.5 shows an example of a typical design file.

■ Table 1.5: Example of a typical design file structure

	Section	Subsection contents
1	Product definition	• Customer information: contact details, technical specification, customer drawings, limitations/constraints on materials to be used • Existing product information: if product is a development of an existing product • Engineering brief: include any notes
2	Product development	• Research information: notes and copies of information found/used • Development notes: notes of any discussions, decisions made • Initial sketches: 2D/3D sketches • Calculation sheets • Brainstorming meeting notes: creative thinking decisions at various stages of the initial design
3	Initial design review	• Initial review meeting notes • Mark-up drawings: initial design drawing with notes added to show any changes proposed • Design check: check design against engineering brief
4	Final design work	• Final drawings: 2D/3D CAD drawings, detailed drawings, circuit diagrams • Calculation sheets • Design notes • Models/prototypes: including photographs showing proposed changes • Material lists: proposed materials to be used
5	Product evaluation	• Product testing: results from testing and inspections • Design check: check design against engineering brief • Product modifications: changes/refinements proposed for the final product • Final product details: final costs of materials and manufacture, time to manufacture • Design sign-off record sheet

ACTIVITY

Working with a partner, create a design file structure on your computer system using its file management system, e.g. Windows Explorer. Create folders for each main section and subfolders for the subsections. Try to keep the title of each folder concise. This will ensure that file names don't become too long.

DID YOU KNOW?

If you start each file management folder name with a number, showing the order that you want the files to be in, the numbers will keep the folders in the correct order.

Once the design file is set up, you are ready to organise all information at each step of the product design process. Organisation of design work in this way is beneficial because:

• information is easier to find and less likely to be lost

• other engineers will be able to find and access information more easily and quickly

• if you were to leave the design process, it would be easier to hand over to another designer.

CHECK MY LEARNING

Managing your design file well is good design housekeeping, and you now have a file system you could use on your product design project. Research 'engineering design file organisation' online and make notes of examples, including how companies name their engineering files.

Initial design using existing products

It is perhaps tempting to start with a clean sheet of paper and sketch out a design, but at an early stage, you should check what has been designed previously. This will help you because you will be able to look at any work done previously.

DID YOU KNOW?

Have you ever heard the saying 'You don't need to reinvent the wheel'?

The term 'don't reinvent the wheel' is often used to prevent time and effort being wasted by someone trying to do something that has already been done, and done successfully. Perhaps not the case with the mountain bike in the photograph!

◻ **Does this product need reinventing?**

Where something has been done well, it is not a simple case of copying the design. The design may be subject to a **patent**.

Researching existing products

You may not be allowed to copy an existing or similar product or someone else's idea. However, there may well be an existing solution out there that you could use as a basis for your design, adjusting it to suit your needs.

It is therefore important to carry out research, to ensure you don't waste time and effort unnecessarily, but also so that you don't invent a square wheel in error.

Research resources

The internet is a great place to find information, although you must take care: not everything is accurate and reliable and information should not be taken at face value. Always double-check any facts.

You will find various textbooks, specialist magazines and online information videos. Most material and equipment suppliers produce catalogues, and many of them also have websites that provide detailed engineering data sheets for their products. Many companies are happy to respond to email requests for information, or even to talk on the telephone.

DID YOU KNOW?

To find technical information, you could use reference sources such as the Machinery's Handbook Guide or the Zeus Booklet for Engineers.

Use your local or school library to help with any research you need to do.

ACTIVITY

Establish which types of resources you have access to:

1 Research and find some online catalogues for mechanical and electronic products and components – there are many available. Check out the types of parts they supply, parts that you could use in an engineering design.

2 Search online for recommended engineering textbooks, covering a variety of engineering disciplines, that a design engineer should have access to.

3 See if your library has any engineering reference textbooks – does it include any of the titles of essential textbooks you identified?

Tap in-house knowledge

Many engineering companies have specialist research and development (R&D) departments where there are engineers who are subject-matter experts. These people have a wealth of knowledge and experience that they would be happy to share with you, if you ask nicely.

Some global/large enterprises even employ specialists whose job is to carry out research and create and manage engineering support databases. This can be a treasure trove of important information for a design engineer.

ACTIVITY

Example of product improvement of an existing product

Take the everyday, common product that is the bicycle. Find pictures of a 'velocipede' and a penny-farthing bicycle and compare them with a modern mountain bike. This is an example of an existing product design that has been developed 'iteratively' over many years. With a partner, write down the similarities and differences between these three products.

Can you think of another product that has undergone major changes, e.g. mobile phones? Find pictures or photographs of three stages in its development – what has changed and what is effectively the same?

CHECK MY LEARNING

It is important that you are aware of existing products and are able to research a product's existing design (if there is one) instead of starting from scratch.

Do you know anyone who is or was involved in engineering? Do they have any old hard-copy textbooks and/or notes that you could look through? You may be able to find electronic versions of these on the internet.

Researching your initial design proposal

KISS ('Keep It Simple, Stupid') is an effective way to start an engineering design. It is often said that the more complex a design is, the more likely it is to go wrong. However, finding a simple solution does not always produce the best product. You will still need to consider the following factors:

- costs of the product
- production times
- product lifecycle
- environmental impact
- safety aspects.

To do this, you need to research the following:

- materials required
- manufacturing processes
- manufacturing skills.

Researching materials for the product

Using more expensive materials might offer improved properties and extended lifetime of the product than using cheaper materials – but is it really necessary? The choice of materials should be appropriate to the intended application, and materials must be readily available. Check that materials:

- are suitable for the environment they will operate in, e.g. in hot areas with high humidity, subject to sunlight or rain, in cold climates, subject to high winds
- can be handled easily and more safely than alternatives; are not fragile, brittle, too soft or too hard to work with; and are suitable for the manufacturing processes that will be used
- do not damage the environment and can be safely disposed of when the product is no longer required
- have a low carbon footprint when they are produced – do they require a lot of energy to produce compared with an alternative material? Can recycled materials be used?

HOW LARGE IS YOUR CARBON FOOTPRINT?

Researching manufacturing processes to be used

The manufacturing processes need to be suitable for the product, but they also need to be available. If the company does not have the machinery or technology to carry out the manufacturing process, then it may have to subcontract the work to another company.

Consider various alternative processes, where possible, and compare their advantages and disadvantages. Some processes will take longer than others; some will have higher associated costs. The required production quantities will have a bearing on this. Check that manufacturing processes:

- are the best option for the material and the design, e.g. does a joint between two materials mean that they need to be bolted or screwed together, or would welding be better?
- are the safest option available
- have a low carbon footprint associated with the energy they use and are environmentally friendly.

Researching manufacturing skills needed

It is important to check that the production department includes people with the necessary skills and that these people are available to carry out the manufacturing processes as shown on the engineering design information, e.g. manufacturing drawings. For example, it may not be sensible to weld every joint on a component, when bolted joints would be satisfactory. The welders could be overloaded with work, while the machining workshop and fitters are left standing idle.

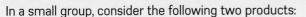

ACTIVITY

In a small group, consider the following two products:

1 wind turbine (on a wind farm)

2 skateboard.

Research the materials used for each product and why they were chosen, as well as how they are joined together. What manufacturing processes and skills were required? Think about safety aspects that could have affected the design (including on-site installation of the wind turbine).

Don't limit yourself when it comes to your initial research. Explore many options; consider all advantages and disadvantages.

However, you will invariably have a limited budget and a very short deadline to meet. Most companies have no choice, if they want to remain competitive.

CHECK MY LEARNING

You should now have an introductory understanding of how to research the design of a product.

With a partner, research manufacturing processes and skills and find out what these are.

Producing initial design sketches in 2D and 3D

Sketches are a useful method of recording and communicating information and have been used for a very long time.

Conveying simple messages in written text is straightforward, but there is often a problem when trying to describe a more complicated design idea, especially if you want someone else, including customers, to understand exactly what you mean. It is sometimes easier to express a concept or an initial engineering idea in a sketch or simple outline drawing. Sketches and drawings have therefore become an important way for engineers to communicate a significant amount of detailed information easily and quickly.

ACTIVITY

Look at Figure 1.8, which shows an abstract sketch of proposed stairs that need to be built. Eventually a detailed engineering drawing will be produced, but, for now, the designer wants to show a customer his thoughts for the best design.

Using the sketch, try to explain in writing what is required for these stairs and then discuss with your class group. How difficult would it be if the sketch had not been produced?

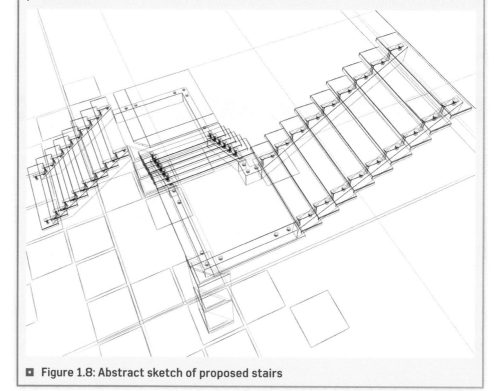

◻ Figure 1.8: Abstract sketch of proposed stairs

Many designers create a series of sketches for their ideas as they progress from their initial idea or concept through to a final design.

Sketches can be neat organised drawings or perhaps doodles or scribbles, but they need to be clear enough to be understood later. Remember not to throw away any design sketches – keep copies in the design file as they may be useful to refer to as the design progresses. It is also important to use annotations in your sketches, so anything not clear is explained in detail. Annotations can also be used for additional detail.

Engineering drawing standards

Sketches and drawings can easily illustrate information about the shape and size of a component or part, and other details such as materials can be identified using simple annotated labels.

Engineering technical drawings are produced to meet the general principles of presentation and the requirements of the British Standards (BS) — national standards produced by the British Standards Institution or BSI Group, which are generally in line with the international standards produced by the International Organization for Standardization (ISO). This means that an engineering drawing, and its dimensions, symbols and tolerances, are easily recognisable and universally understood, without the issue of language difficulties between different countries.

Design sketches are not limited by these engineering standards. However, producing sketches in a specific way, using preferred practices, certainly helps to communicate your ideas better.

Design sketches in 2D and 3D

Like engineering drawings, design sketches can be produced in 2D and 3D. Which you choose for your design idea will depend on what you are trying to portray. Experience will eventually tell you the best way, and if you need to produce both types of sketch.

2D

Concept sketches in 2D are normally created first. Orthographic (or orthogonal) projections, where the outline of an object is 'projected' onto a flat plane using parallel lines, are normally used to show three views: a front view, a side view and a plan (top or bottom) view.

Figure 1.9 shows an example of a 2D drawing with an orthographic projection of a component in three views.

3D

2D sketches are sometimes difficult to understand. If looking at the side view, which side is shown? Does the plan view show the top or bottom? People with limited spatial awareness may find 2D sketches confusing. 3D sketches and drawings provide a better visual image of an object. The three methods of 3D sketching – oblique projections, isometric projections (see Figure 1.10) and perspective drawings – are described in more detail in Component 3.

Top view

Front view   Side view

■ **Figure 1.9: Orthographic projection**

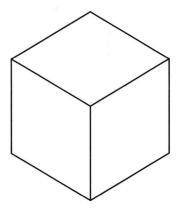

■ **Figure 1.10: 3D sketch of a cube (isometric projection)**

ACTIVITY

Practise your sketching:

1 Create a 3D sketch of the component in Figure 1.9.

2 Take the 3D sketch of the cube in Figure 1.10 and add spots to the three sides showing, to turn the cube into a dice. (Remember, opposite sides must add up to seven.)

3 Now create a 2D sketch of the dice, showing how all sides need to look for it to be made.

CHECK MY LEARNING ■ ■ ■

You have now been introduced to the purpose and benefits of sketching initial design ideas. Think of a new product, perhaps your innovation from previous lessons, and produce 2D and 3D sketches for it. Discuss with your class.

Creative thinking and evaluation techniques

In everyday life, creativity is more often used to describe people associated with the arts – artists, authors, actors and music composers. However, many great designers have used their creativity to generate and develop their ideas. Creative thinking is all about thinking in new ways to solve a problem, especially when answers do not always appear spontaneously. **Thinking outside the box** is a term commonly associated with creative thinking.

KEY TERM

Thinking outside the box means thinking in an original or creative way.

As with most things, there is one rule that should always be observed – always write down an idea before you forget it!

Using creative thinking and evaluation techniques

You can start to generate ideas using various creativity tools to help you consider and solve problems. Remember, there is no right or wrong method of thinking and of recording ideas and thoughts – use whatever suits you and in whatever way you understand best.

The following are some of the tools you could use for creative thinking.

- Reword the problem. Try writing out the problem in several different ways, to see if this makes it clearer what is actually required.

- Hold a brainstorming group session to come up with potential solutions. Bring in people who understand the problem, but also invite others. Sometimes 'outsiders' can have the most interesting ideas.

- Present the problem visually to find a solution. You might want to draw a diagram or produce a mind map (see Figure 1.11).

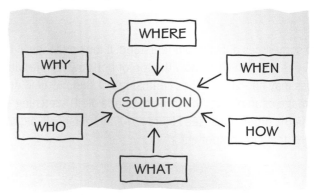

◻ Figure 1.11: Mind map to find the solution

- Challenge your own assumptions. Try to look at the problem from different perspectives. Just because something has traditionally been done in a certain way, it does not mean that it cannot be improved.

- Think in reverse. Instead of thinking about a potential solution, think about how the problem might have been created in the first place. This can be an effective way of stimulating new ideas.

- Develop a rich picture. This is a way of gathering information in pictorial form. Draw several little diagrams to illustrate ideas and issues around a central theme. Many people respond better to graphical stimuli than to the written word.
- Try the de Bono Group's Six Thinking Hats® to generate fresh ideas (see Figure 1.12). Global/large companies use this technique to develop ideas and products, and it requires a teamwork approach to make it successful.

 The Green Hat: focuses on creativity, possibilities, alternatives and new ideas. It is an opportunity to express new concepts and new perceptions – lateral thinking could be used here.

 The Blue Hat: is used to manage the thinking process. It ensures that the 'Six Thinking Hats' guidelines are observed.

 The Red Hat: signifies feelings, hunches and intuition. It is where emotions are placed without explanation.

 The White Hat: calls for information known or needed. "The facts, just the facts."

 The Yellow Hat: symbolises brightness and optimism. You can explore the positives and probe for value and benefits.

 The Black Hat: signifies caution and critical thinking – do not overuse! Consider why something may not work.

☑ **Figure 1.12: De Bono's six hats**

Design is a process of constant evaluation

Continuous evaluation is necessary throughout the design process to assess and appraise how the design is progressing. There is a wide range of methods and types of design evaluation. The most common types are formative and summative.

Formative evaluation

Formative evaluation is carried out before the design process starts and then again during the implementation stages of design. The aim is to provide continual improvement of the design and to ensure the design is carried out efficiently and effectively. Terms such as proactive, interactive and monitoring evaluations describe some of the formative evaluation types.

Summative evaluation

Summative evaluation is used following the implementation stages of design and is used to assess whether the design has met its objectives, whether there are unforeseen problems, and what could be improved now or possibly in the future. Terms such as outcome evaluation represent this type of evaluation.

ACTIVITY

Working with a partner, research 'mind maps' and 'rich pictures' online and make notes.

ACTIVITY

You can find more detailed information about design evaluation and its terms by looking online at some examples of the different types.

With the rest of the class, watch a video on de Bono's six hats, and then discuss.

CHECK MY LEARNING

As a class, discuss what you now understand by creative thinking and constant evaluation. Think about the different types of evaluation. Create a table to record a score out of ten against each of the required elements of the engineering brief. Adding up the total score indicates how successful the solution is overall. This can be used as a framework for evaluating ideas during the design process.

Computer-aided design (CAD) drawings

Computer-aided design (CAD) is now the most common tool used to create 2D and 3D design drawings. Prior to its introduction, engineered product designs were drawn up by highly skilled technical draughtspersons who worked at large drawing boards, the height and angle of which could be adjusted to suit the individual draughtsperson.

DID YOU KNOW?

The term 'back to the drawing board' was, and is sometimes still, used to mean literally what it says. It is a phrase used to indicate that a design or plan has failed and a new one needs to be devised from the beginning.

Now most design drawings, including sketches and simple outline drawings, can be created more easily and quickly using CAD package software, which gives the draughtsperson the ability to save, modify and print whole design drawings or sections/parts of designs whenever required.

CAD packages

Some companies still create design drawings on paper. But many, including global/large organisations, SMEs and small jobbing companies, use CAD to create their design drawings and documentation electronically. CAD has major advantages, including:

- quicker and easier to complete a drawing and print paper copies
- storage facilities are smaller and it is quicker to find and access designs
- convenience of transferring files, e.g. via email or converting to a **PDF** file
- files can be linked directly to computer numerical control (CNC) machines and 3D printers.

The CAD package software has to be learned by the user, in the same way that the technical draughtsperson working at a drawing board has to learn their skills. This may take some time, depending on the software used and the complexity of the drawings that are to be produced. A knowledge of manual drawing skills is normally of great benefit, as these skills can also be used with CAD, especially when it comes to arranging the layout of a drawing and using standard drawing terms and symbols.

There are many CAD packages available, from small, free software packages to complex packages costing thousands of pounds. Usually the more expensive the software package, the greater the scope of commands the software will have, but the longer the learning curve will be.

Most CAD packages use standard commands to draw, modify and edit design drawings, using standard templates for different categories of engineering drawing (see Figure 1.13).

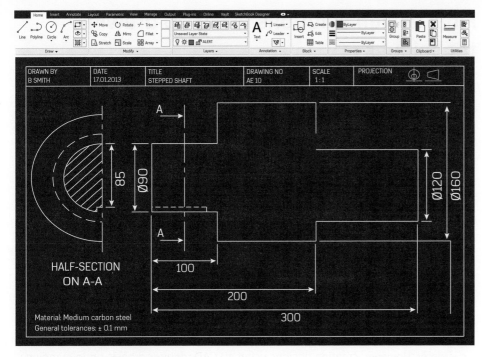

Command structures

CAD packages, like most software, generally have a specific set of commands, although some commands may be labelled differently. For example, some CAD packages refer to symbols as objects. Some of the more general commands for AutoCAD® packages, for example, are included in Table 1.6.

■ Table 1.6: General AutoCAD® commands

Commands	Used to
Draw commands	**Draw** – draw lines, circles, arcs and standard geometry
Edit commands	**Erase** – erase objects and mistakes
	Copy – copy objects and details
	Mirror – create a reverse or mirror image
	Move – move an object around the drawing
	Rotate – rotate an object around a point
	Trim – trim part of an object

ACTIVITY

It can take a while to get used to CAD software. You will need to find out which CAD system you will be using and then, with a partner, begin to become familiar with the software.

Try to produce simple lines and circles and also to erase, copy and move objects within the drawing template.

Look at some of the other commands available and find out, by researching online, what these commands are for.

CHECK MY LEARNING

You have been introduced to CAD drawing. Once you have had a chance to try out the software, discuss with your partner the benefits of using CAD, compared with manual drawing and sketching.

Final design solutions using 2D drawing techniques

In the previous lesson, some of the more general CAD commands were mentioned. There are, of course, many more, but it takes time to become familiar with each command's functions. Generally, all CAD packages will have an instruction book that lists the commands. In time, you will begin to recognise each command without needing to refer to the instructions, and this will help you to work faster and more efficiently.

It may well be worth making your own notes about essential information and important commands to help you develop your knowledge and skills. Remember, as well, when using any computer software, ensure you keep passwords safe!

2D design drawings

There are many benefits of using 3D design instead of 2D. Some of the advantages were mentioned previously. 3D designs are normally easier to visualise and less confusing. 3D images can be of significant benefit when trying to assess if there are any problems with a new product during its development or when showing a design to a customer. However, creating designs using 3D CAD requires a basic understanding of 2D CAD principles, so it is best to start with and master, at least, the basic commands of 2D CAD. This might take some time.

Basic activities and commands

To create a 2D design drawing with CAD, there are some basic activities and commands that you will need to understand and become familiar with. Some to get you started are listed in Table 1.7.

◻ Table 1.7: Some basic activities and commands for CAD

Activity	Commands
1 Set up a design	• Set the drawing size to A4, A3, A2 or A1 (these are paper sizes for printing – you will need to decide which size is best for your design) • Set grid size to 10 mm squares • Set snap command to 1 mm increments • Select line types: centre, dashed
2 Draw simple items	• Use line, circle, polygon commands
3 Master the edit and display commands – you will use these a lot	• Edit commands: such as erase, copy, mirror, move • Display commands: such as zoom and pan
4 Use text	• Text is important. You will need to annotate your drawings and input your name, the drawing name and details, etc. in the drawing template's title block
5 As you become more familiar, try other commands	• Other line types: input a fillet (radius) to two lines and add a chamfer • Dimensions: between two points, for a radius
6 Create a simple engineering drawing	• Dimension the drawing using the system's automatic commands

It is important to remember to save your drawing regularly as you work. Otherwise, you could lose many hours of work if the computer crashes or there is a power cut.

You should create a file/folder on your computer in which to save and file your drawing. This file/folder could be added to the engineering design file mentioned previously. The drawing file needs to have a completely new name, and you should make sure that you do not overwrite previous file names, as these files will then be lost. At various stages in the design process, save your drawing work, giving the drawing file name a new version number so that old work is not overwritten and lost.

ACTIVITY

Practise 2D CAD drawing by opening a new drawing template (see, for example, Figure 1.14), assigning and saving a new file name and version number, and trying out the basic activities and commands.

When you are feeling more confident and comfortable with using the basic commands, create a 2D design drawing of a product or component. Perhaps select one of the items you manually sketched in 2D previously, e.g. a dice, or an innovation idea you have been working on.

Once complete, print out your design drawing and discuss any areas of concern you still have with your teacher.

■ Figure 1.14: CAD drawing template

CHECK MY LEARNING

You have now tried basic 2D CAD drawing and have an idea of some of the many commands.

Watch a video of how some CAD packages, such as SolidWorks®, can be used to convert a 2D drawing into a 3D one.

Try to create a 3D CAD drawing of a simple cube. Discuss any difficulties with a partner.

Generating final design drawings

GETTING STARTED

With a partner, discuss the types of drawing you think are used in engineering and the information each could provide.

Drawings are created for many purposes. For example, they can be used to show the plans of housing estates, the layout of engineering process plants, manufacturing details to make component parts, and the design of electronic circuits.

There is a wide variety of engineering drawings that are used to show the technical details of an engineered component, part or product. The drawings used to make an engineered product are often called engineering working drawings and generally fall into the following commonly known categories:

- sketches
- component drawings
- assembly drawings
- parts lists/drawings
- circuit diagrams.

Sketches

The use of sketches to illustrate concepts and ideas, and the benefits of doing so, have been mentioned previously.

- 2D sketches, using orthographic projections, are used to show the outline of a component or part, usually showing a front, side and plan view.
- 3D sketches are used to create a better visual image of an object, normally using oblique or isometric projections, or perspective drawings.

ACTIVITY

Do some research to find the differences between oblique and isometric projections and perspective drawings. Discuss with your partner.

Component drawings

Component drawings provide information needed to manufacture a component or part, including materials, dimensions and surface finishes required. They can also provide details of any design features, such as where holes should be drilled and/or a thread needs to be formed.

As detail is important, most component drawings will be produced in 2D orthographic projections with views of all sides of the component. Drawings for complex component designs may include a 3D view of the component to help visualise how the component should look when finished.

Assembly drawings

Component drawings do not show how each component will be used. An assembly drawing is required to show how each component interacts with other components. These may be drawn in 2D or 3D, whichever communicates what is required in the best way. Drawings may be created for the main assembly and for any sub-assemblies and will include information such as how component parts should be joined, e.g. welded or bolted connections.

In cases where clarity is required, some assembly drawings are produced to show 3D exploded views.

Parts lists/drawings

The individual components and parts in an assembly drawing must be easily identified. This usually means that each component or part is given a reference number that then relates to a numbered item in a table of parts, normally in one corner of the drawing.

For complicated assemblies, there might be an engineering parts drawing specifically to identify each part. In addition to showing how the product is assembled, the list may be used by production engineers to plan the work and purchase materials and other parts.

Circuit diagrams

Designs that include electronic circuits will need a circuit schematic diagram. This is drawn using lines and symbols that represent electrical components, such as a resistor or a capacitor. Some CAD design packages have a library of symbols ready to be selected and added to the drawing. Figure 1.15 shows a simple electronic circuit.

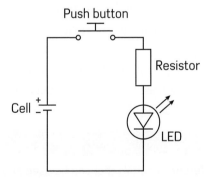

◘ **Figure 1.15: Simple circuit schematic diagram**

LINK IT UP

To find out more about the methods of 3D sketching and making engineering working drawings, go to Component 3.

Final design solutions using 3D printing

■ **3D printing**

Additive manufacturing

3D printing, also known as additive manufacturing (AM), is a rapidly developing technology that is being used to create 3D objects and models, and is also being used to make parts for engineered products.

Traditional machine workshop processes, such as those using lathes and milling machines, remove material and are called subtractive manufacturing processes. Additive manufacturing is when materials are melted and then added layer by layer to produce the 3D object needed.

3D products can be created with a CAD package. The main advantage of 3D printing from CAD is that it reduces mistakes. A 3D design model can be created with CAD and then checked before printing is started.

3D printer resolution

CAD software will slice up your model into layers of various thicknesses. If the layers are too thin, it will take a long time to print the model. If the layers are too thick, the model may end up with rough edges and lack fine details.

3D printers use x, y, z coordinates, as in Figure 1.16. Coordinates x and y are planar dimensions, i.e. relative to the flat plane, while z refers to the height of each layer. The x,y **resolution** affects the feature size and the z resolution affects the layer height.

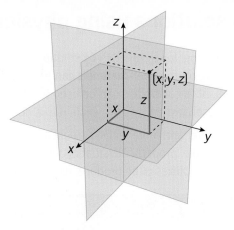

□ Figure 1.16: 3D printing *x*, *y*, *z* coordinates

To create good 3D printing models by FDM, you may need to look at the considerations described in Table 1.8.

□ Table 1.8: Actions to consider when 3D printing

Considerations	Reason or actions needed
Drawings and designs sometimes need modifying	This is due to the way 3D printers add material to the engineered product
Overhangs on the printed model will need support	Imagine a set of aircraft wings: they will not support their own weight when the plastic is hot, so a support structure will be needed underneath to prevent the mould from breaking
There will be shrinkage from the original design	The model will need to be made oversize so that the final size is correct
There will be surplus plastic deposited on the model	This will need removing with hand tools
CAD files may be corrupted when transferred to the printer	CAD files will need to be repaired
Printer resolution settings	The lower the resolution is set, the rougher the finish The higher it is set, the smoother the finish, but the machining process will be very slow
Different colours can be moulded	Be aware that they can melt together into an ugly grey or brown colour
You can scan engineered products	To get a good scan, the resolution needs to be set very high, but this means a slow process You will need to create a mirror image of the scan

ACTIVITY

Working in small groups, consider a simple product you could make on a 3D printer. You will need to sketch the product, then create a CAD drawing of the product to be printed. Consider any issues associated with the materials to be used, support structures needed, and the time it will take to create the product.

CHECK MY LEARNING

You have had a basic introduction to 3D printing. With a partner, list and then sketch three engineered products that could be produced on a 3D printer.

Final design solutions using physical modelling

As an alternative to 3D printing, for certain design solutions and product prototypes, 3D physical modelling using off-the-shelf materials can be easier and quicker and cost less. Like all 3D solutions, physical models can be used to show what an idea will look like; they are particularly useful when trying to explain to a non-technical person.

3D models give a much clearer and more realistic visual image of an item than looking over a 2D drawing. For example, property developers of large, new housing estates or office buildings and retail complexes often produce 3D layout models to sell their plans.

ACTIVITY

If you answered yes to making a physical model before, sketch your idea on the whiteboard and discuss what you did with your class.

Physical modelling

The size of a physical model very much depends on the purpose for which it is being built. Is the model required to show more clearly what an engineered product will look like, or is it to help identify any problems with the design? Models that are simplistic in approach may lose some of the desired accuracy.

Physical models may be of a single component or part of an overall product. Models may be built smaller or larger than the actual size of the planned engineered product, or sometimes to the same size as the finished product.

There are various materials that can be used for physical modelling. For example, card, plastics, wood, metal, or a combination of these can be used. Using scrap materials and parts might also be worth considering. The materials selected need to fit in with any restrictions on cost and time.

◘ Car made of corrugated card

Materials may have adhesion problems, different wear rates, different limits of expansion and contraction, and other limitations. For example, card is not very waterproof. The materials chosen for the model need to be easy to shape and easy to modify.

Some modelling materials may lack the realism of 3D printing, and so 3D printing techniques should also be considered for the physical model. It might make sense to make some parts by 3D printing and combine them with other materials. Table 1.9 shows a selection of modelling materials along with some of their advantages and disadvantages.

◘ **Table 1.9: The advantages and disadvantages of some modelling materials**

Modelling material	Advantages	Disadvantages
Card	• Cheap • Material is readily available • Models can be made quickly and easily • Only basic skills are required	• Models often lack realism • Difficult to produce to an exact **scale**
Plastics	• Cheap • Most materials are readily available; some may need to be obtained from specialist suppliers • Easier to produce to scale	• High skill levels required for intricate models • Shrinkage is possible and must be considered • May require intricate, expensive moulds to be manufactured in wood or other materials
Wood	• Relatively cheap • Most materials are readily available • Can be produced to scale	• High skill levels required for intricate models • Special tools and skills required • Takes more time to produce
Metals	• Most materials are readily available from specialist suppliers • Can be produced to scale	• High skill levels required for intricate models • Often expensive machinery required for machining • Expensive and takes time to produce

Making final design solution decisions on materials

Although materials will have been explored during the design process and may have affected the way in which the design has progressed, there will be a final decision to make on this important factor. Have you selected the best materials? Are they available and **sustainable** and do they have **longevity** and durability?

KEY TERMS

Sustainability refers to the ability of something to be maintained at a specific level.
Longevity means a long life.

Selection of materials

In a perfect world, it should be easy to identify the best material for an engineered product. The preferred material chosen to make a product will depend on several factors or criteria, such as material strength, hardness, magnetism or conductivity. For example, a standard polymer would not be chosen for an electrical circuit because most polymers do not conduct electricity. Gold, silver, copper or, occasionally, aluminium would be selected instead. However, cost factors would probably determine that copper should be specified as it gives the best **conductivity** per **unit cost**. On an intricate printed circuit board (PCB) design, gold plating for contacts may be specified as gold is an excellent conductor.

KEY TERMS

Conductivity is the ability of a material to conduct electricity.
Unit cost is the cost of one item, e.g. if 10 m of pipe costs £20, the unit cost is £2 per metre.

Categories of materials

The components and parts of an engineered product will generally be made from four categories of engineering material. These are:

- ferrous metals, e.g. mild steel, stainless steel, wrought iron
- non-ferrous metals, e.g. aluminium, titanium, copper
- thermosetting polymers, e.g. phenol-formaldehyde, polyimides, polyurethane
- thermoforming polymers, e.g. polyethylene, polypropylene, acrylic.

LINK IT UP

Details of engineering material categories and their properties and characteristics are covered further in Components 2 and 3.

Assessment of materials

It is sometimes tricky to judge and decide on the best material to use. It is often sensible to compare materials objectively. A simple method is to decide on the basis of important criteria, assessing and scoring each material against each criterion. For example, a score of 5 would be good and 0 would be poor. The highest overall score indicates the best selection.

Example

It is essential that a component is lightweight and corrosion resistant, and its size needs to be 30 mm in diameter and 200 mm long. The material choices are: mild steel, copper, aluminium and polyethylene. Table 1.10 indicates the initial considerations.

◻ **Table 1.10: Initial assessment of materials**

Materials	Considerations
Mild steel	Too heavy, not corrosion resistant, but 30 mm diameter is available in stores
Copper	Too expensive and not available
Aluminium	Light, so weight OK, but required diameter not available
Polyethylene (PE)	Light, inexpensive, but only 35 mm diameter PE rod is available in stores

From this comparison, it is difficult to decide which material is the best option.

Table 1.11, however, can be used to help clarify the situation, by scoring each material against specific criteria of weight, availability, unit cost and corrosion resistance.

◻ **Table 1.11: Objective comparison of materials**

Criteria	Mild steel	Copper	Aluminium	Polyethylene
Weight	1	3	4	5
Availability	5	0	0	0
Unit cost	3	5	4	5
Corrosion resistance	0	5	5	5
Total	9	13	13	15

This suggests that polyethylene would be the best option, even though it is not available in the required 30 mm diameter.

There is a further option, and this would be to machine the 35 mm diameter polyethylene rod down to the required 30 mm diameter. The zero-availability score would become 5, although the cost of machining the polyethylene would reduce the unit cost to a score of 3. The polyethylene overall score would still be the best, at 18.

This assessment raised questions that were answered with a little bit of engineering thought and analysis.

ACTIVITY

Building on previous lesson activities and the development of a new engineered product, and working with a partner, take your design drawings and consider the best materials for the product. List the essential criteria for the material and assess the material options available.

CHECK MY LEARNING

You have now looked at how to make decisions associated with the final selection of engineering materials. Discuss any thoughts you have with your class group.

Making final design solution decisions on making techniques

GETTING STARTED

Discuss in a group the factors that can affect the final design solution decision for the selection of making techniques.

Once again, even though making techniques will have been explored during the design process and, as with materials selection, may have affected the way in which the design has progressed, there will still be a final decision to be made. Are the making techniques the right choice? Are the skills available and are they also sustainable?

Selection of making techniques

The selection of a making technique is influenced by the material type and its form or shape. For example, to reduce the diameter of a mild steel cylindrical component, carrying out a turning process on a lathe is the preferred option. Flat or square features would be best achieved on a milling machine.

Materials that are large in size and will not fit on a machine may need to be manufactured using hand tools.

Categories of making techniques

A whole range of manufacturing processes is normally used to ensure that an engineered product is made correctly and to the highest possible standards.

The processes will generally be grouped into four categories of making techniques. These are:

- cutting processes: drilling, sawing, filing, shearing
- shaping processes: turning, milling
- forming processes: casting, forging, extruding, moulding
- joining and fabrication processes: fastening, bonding, soldering, brazing/welding.

In addition to mechanical engineering processes, there may also be a need for electrical or electronic engineering processes to be carried out.

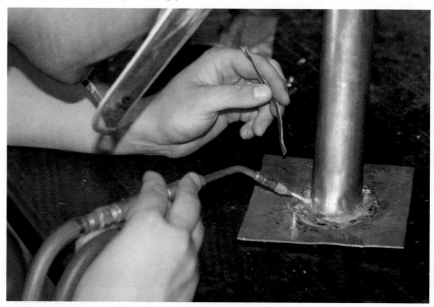

LINK IT UP

Details of engineering making techniques and manufacturing processes, as well as examples of their use, are covered further in Components 2 and 3.

◻ **Trainee plumber learning how to solder**

Assessment of making techniques

As mentioned already, the processes required to cut, shape, form or join and fabricate the material will provide an indication of the types of making techniques that need to be used.

Example

Consider the example in the previous lesson. Ultimately, it was decided that the best material option was to reduce the diameter of 35 mm polyethylene rod down to the required 30 mm diameter. Table 1.12 indicates the initial considerations for the making techniques to accomplish this.

◘ Table 1.12: Assessment of making techniques

Making techniques	Considerations
Turning (on a lathe)	Cylindrical component, so ideal for turning
Milling (on a milling machine)	Possible, but milling is better for producing flat square surfaces
Filing and sawing	Not ideal as it would be difficult to make using hand tools

◘ Turning polyethylene on a lathe

This suggests that turning the polyethylene on a lathe would be the best option.

ACTIVITY

With the same partner as in the previous lesson, continue with the same activity in which you selected materials for an engineered product, and decide on the making techniques required. List any essential criteria for the making techniques and assess all options available.

CHECK MY LEARNING

You have now looked at how to make decisions associated with the final selection of engineering making techniques.

Do you think it is possible to apply a similar objective comparison for the selection of making techniques as was done for the materials? Try to create a table for such a comparison and then discuss with your class group.

Considering quality requirements

Whether quality is defined as a statement of how good or bad something is, that something is made to a high standard, or that something is 'fit for purpose', quality is an important part of our everyday lives. Quality applies to the products we manufacture and the services we provide.

Meeting customer requirements

Engineered products need to meet customer requirements – a specific feature or set of attributes that are needed or wanted by the customer. To do this, a product needs to:

- do what the customer expects it to do, e.g. the product functions as it is designed to do
- have an appearance that the customer expects it to have, e.g. correct colour, size
- be well built, e.g. correct materials, correct weight
- be reliable, e.g. last for an expected length of time
- be safe to use.

The list could go on and on. There are many other 'requirements' or 'expectations' that could be added to this list.

Quality assurance

When engineered products are made, they need to conform to the specified requirements. It is also necessary for products to be manufactured to a consistent standard – so that each item or copy of the product is made and functions in the same way, every time.

The quality of the product needs to be controlled. This control is relevant to all stages of a product's manufacture: its development, design and production.

Quality is also a term used to measure or compare something, such as an engineered product, against other similar things or products.

Many companies have quality assurance (QA) departments whose responsibility is to strictly control the quality of all products – by rigorously checking that the products conform to the specified requirements, have no faults or deficiencies and, ultimately, are acceptable to the customer. A fault would commonly be referred to as a 'non-conformance'.

Quality control

A company's QA department will have set procedures for carrying out quality control (QC) checks on engineered parts, components, assemblies and products to ensure they conform to their design specifications – that they are fit for purpose. The checks will depend on the type of product, but generally will include all or some of the inspections and tests shown in Table 1.13.

■ Table 1.13: Example of standard quality control checks for an engineered product

Inspections and tests	Quality checks
Visual checks	• Correct materials used? • Acceptable surface finish – too rough or too smooth? (Use surface texture gauges) • Correct colour? • No rough or sharp edges? • Item is free of damage?
Dimensional checks	• Dimensions are as per the design drawing? (Use measuring equipment, e.g. engineer's rule, engineer's squares) • Dimensions are within specified tolerances? (Use callipers, micrometers, special gauges) • Features in the correct positions, e.g. drilled holes, threaded holes? • Features correct, e.g. threaded holes have the correct thread? (Check with thread gauges) • Product's weight is correct? (Use a beam or digital balance/scales)
Final inspections and product testing	• Individual components fit together and align with each other where required? • Electrical/electronic circuits work? (Check using a multimeter) • The product functions as specified? (Carry out a functional test, record times if important) • Ergonomics of the product design is acceptable? • Product is safe to operate?

LINK IT UP

Inspection and testing of a design solution, as well as measurement skills, are covered in Component 2. Measuring equipment is also covered in Component 3.

During the making process, it is extremely important to carry out checks periodically, particularly checking critical dimensions.

ACTIVITY

With the same partner as in the previous lesson, continue with the activity in which you have already selected materials and making techniques for an engineered product. Now decide on the quality checks you believe will be required to ensure that the product meets the required specification. Create a checklist similar to Table 1.13, with a column to tick off when each check has been completed.

Present your checklist to the class and discuss.

CHECK MY LEARNING

Considering quality requirements and carrying out quality control checks are essential functions in every company. Discuss with your class why it is so important, including why it is important to carry out checks periodically throughout manufacturing.

Look around your classroom and select any product. Write out a quality control checklist for this product.

Working in a team and peer review

All employees work in a team.

Of course, there are times when employees may need to work individually, such as when performing a design calculation, producing a CAD drawing or operating workshop machinery equipment. There are numerous examples of other individual working processes. However, the work each employee does is part of the overall picture, which for an engineering company is all about producing an engineered product.

Teamwork

Teamwork is where two or more people work in a collaborative way, combining their efforts to achieve a specific, common objective. Many companies encourage **team building** within their normal working processes and procedures to improve employee morale, cooperation and trust.

KEY TERM

Team building is a method of getting employees to work together as an effective team.

The benefits of teamwork include:

- keeping everyone involved, supporting and encouraging employees in carrying out their individual work activities
- increasing individual and team motivation
- encouraging communication
- sharing information and knowledge, helping to solve difficult problems and finding a wider range of practical solutions
- supporting innovative thinking and creativity, encouraging employees to think of more unconventional ideas
- sharing ownership of failed plans or initiatives – often part of product development.

Project teams

In addition to everyday teamwork within a company, some teams may be pulled together to complete a specific task or a special project, such as the development of a new product or work procedure. The team may be made up of people who do not normally work together. For example:

- design engineers
- manufacturing engineers
- production/machine operators
- quality control engineers.

In this case, the new project team members will need to get used to working with each other, which may take a little time.

Peer review

It is important to discuss ideas and get opinions from others in your team. Valuable contributions can be made by your peers.

Peers

A peer is someone with the same knowledge and abilities as you. You must make allowances and try to understand the strengths and limitations of your peers and other team members when you are working together.

Peer review methods

Peer review methods are often used to ensure that a company's standards of quality are being maintained and to help analyse where performance can be improved.

In engineering product development, peer reviews may be carried out by a team of peers, each with the responsibility to review a specific aspect of product development and find a satisfactory solution for any associated design issues.

ACTIVITY

Working in teams of four people, assign a role to each team member corresponding to one of the four team responsibilities: design engineer, manufacturing engineer, production/machine operator, quality control engineer. Consider an engineered product and, within your role, think of a problem area, perhaps one that is commonly encountered. Write a short brief outlining how you would overcome the problem.

Next, swap your briefs with those of another team; each team should then peer review the other team's results by making comments on the briefs. Comment only on the brief related to your role. Once completed, similar roles should discuss each other's peer reviewed briefs.

CHECK MY LEARNING

You have now learned about teamwork and peer reviews. As a class group, discuss how you found the peer review process. Working in a team can be difficult unless everyone shares a common positive attitude, including acceptance of criticism.

Using generic work skills

Working with others can be challenging, but you must respect their ideas, even if they are contrary to your own. Whether you are dealing with work colleagues or a customer, or with a supplier or representative of another company, you must always conduct yourself in a professional way and with a positive attitude.

Generic skills

When looking to employ someone for a job position, employers will look at qualifications, but they will also look for people who have generic skills, sometimes referred to as transferable skills.

Behaviour

These are skills that normally have to be learned and practised often. You should be able to:

- communicate effectively: write and speak clearly and listen carefully
- set targets and keep to them, including being reliable and punctual for work.

Management of time is important. If you run into problems and don't let anyone know about it, this could impact negatively on other parts of the company.

Attitude

Positive attitude can say a lot. A negative attitude will get you remembered, perhaps for something you would rather it didn't. You should be able to:

- make constructive suggestions
- not be put off by setbacks and problems.

When asked to do something, try saying, 'I'd be happy to.'

Limitations

Know your limitations and work within them. You should be able to:

- understand clearly your tasks
- understand clearly your responsibilities.

Discuss any problems with colleagues as soon as they become a concern.

Respect for others

You may not agree with other people's opinions, but that does not mean you should violently disagree with them. You should be able to:

- accept criticism, put your arguments together slowly and clearly, and present them in a clear and concise manner
- value the opinions of others, change your mind where necessary, and maybe adopt some of their ideas.

Respect is about listening to and evaluating other people's points of view.

Professionalism

Professionalism is about acting responsibly and responsively. You should be able to act:

- with respect
- with honesty
- with **integrity**
- in an **ethical** way.

Be prepared to invest time and effort in learning new skills. Many engineers continue their own professional development throughout their careers.

KEY TERMS

Integrity is the quality of having moral principles.
Ethical means something that is morally good or right to do.

☐ Professionalism

Working relationships

It is important to build a good working relationship with your colleagues. You should be able to share your knowledge and skills to help others.

Collaborative skills

Collaboration is essential to a company's productivity. You should be able to:

- cooperate with others
- be part of the company team
- recognise the contributions of others.

ACTIVITY

Working with a partner, search online for some more generic employment skills that you think are important in engineering. Make notes on them. Get together in small groups to discuss and list any new skills you discovered on a whiteboard.

Discuss generic skills with the rest of the class group.

CHECK MY LEARNING

You should now be familiar with some of the generic skills that employers look for.

Write a list of the skills you think you are good at, and those you may need to work on improving.

Learning aim B: assessment practice

How you will be assessed

In Component 1 you will be assessed by completing a series of internally set assignments.

You will need to show that you understand the different aspects related to engineering skills and how they can be used throughout the design process. This will include demonstrating a detailed understanding of:

- the engineering design process: defining the problem, developing possible solutions, choosing a solution, designing and modelling the solution, evaluating the outcome and working in a team.

CHECKPOINT

Strengthen
- Outline the activities carried out in each stage of the engineering design process.

Challenge
- Evaluate the importance of each stage of the engineering design process in ensuring a successful outcome which meets the needs of a product design brief.

ASSESSMENT ACTIVITY   LEARNING AIM   **A**

Description
In this assignment you will be asked to follow the engineering design process to provide a solution to a given product design brief. This will include developing possible proposals, choosing a solution, modelling the solution, evaluating the outcome and working in a team.

Example tasks

You are provided with the following product design brief for a drill bit storage device. The drill bit storage device must:

1 provide safe, secure storage for a set of 25 drill bits ranging in size range from 1mm to 13mm in 0.5mm increments

2 enable quick and easy identification, selection, removal and replacement of drill bits

3 protect stored drill bits from swarf/dust/dirt

4 be robust and impact resistant

5 be corrosion resistant.

You must interpret the requirements of this brief and then:

- use the Internet to investigate if there are any products on the market that would be suitable or are similar

- produce some detailed 2D/3D sketches of at least two different design proposals (your initial design ideas) - these should include detailed annotations to show how they fully meet the requirements of the brief

- choose one proposal and give detailed reasons why it is the best, with specific reference to the brief.

Having decided which of your proposals is the best, you now need to develop this into a completed solution to the initial brief. To do this, you must use CAD software to produce fully dimensioned engineering drawings to an appropriate standard of your chosen design solution - make sure you produce a list or screen shots of all the drawing, editing, modification and manipulation commands you use as you go along. You must also create a 3D model of your chosen design solution. Once you have done this, make sure you have specified materials, making processes and quality requirements for your chosen design solution, giving detailed, accurate reasons for your decisions.

All of your work should be put into a design folder. Having produced your design folder, you now need to review your work so far with a group of colleagues. To do this:

- set up a design review meeting to provide detailed feedback to your colleagues about your design solution and how it meets all the elements of the engineering brief - your feedback should include the use of written commentary, graphics and verbal communication

- get your colleagues to review your design solution using a peer review form

- review their thoughts about whether your design solution has any flaws (e.g. do they think it meets the requirements of the client needs? Can it be made?)

Finally, you need to look at all of the evidence you have gathered so far and present further ideas for the development of your design solution, with reasons why they are improvements report on how the whole design process, including interpreting the brief, preparing design proposals, utilising all types of feedback and using a range of modification tools, has helped the final solution to meet the client needs

Evidence

Evidence could include:

- a design folder – including findings from your investigation about similar products, fully annotated 2D and 3D sketches, CAD drawings and a list or screen shots of all CAD commands you used, images of your 3D modelling/models, notes about materials, making processes and quality requirements for the solution.

- written commentary/graphics from your design review meeting and the peer review forms.

- ideas for the further development of your design solution.

- a report on how the design process has helped the final solution to meet the engineering brief/client needs.

TIPS

- Make sure you read the assignment brief, and write notes about what you need to do.
- Ensure you understand the brief.
- Store your evidence safely.

TAKE IT FURTHER

Carry out the changes to your design solution that were suggested during your review meeting and make a 3D model of the improved design. Prepare a presentation that could be used alongside your model to present the final design solution to your client.

2 Investigating an Engineering Project

Introduction

How does an engineered product get made? What materials are needed and what characteristics and properties do they have? When entering the world of engineering, you will need to know certain key information – for example, the types of materials and their characteristics, the different types of components and the making processes that support the manufacture of engineered products.

In this component, you will develop your understanding of the types and properties of metallic and polymeric materials and proprietary components commonly used in engineered products.

Once you have understood how designers use their knowledge of materials, proprietary components, making processes and disassembly, you yourself will plan, reproduce, inspect and test a single component.

If you are entering the industry as an engineer, this component will help you to gain a keen understanding of some of the most important aspects of engineering practice that will be invaluable to you in the future.

LEARNING AIMS

In this component you will:

A	understand materials, components and processes for a given engineered product
B	investigate a given engineered product using disassembly techniques
C	plan the manufacture of and safely reproduce/inspect/test a given engineered component.

Engineering materials: ferrous metals

Different materials offer many different design opportunities for an engineer. The properties of different materials make them suitable for different uses and manufacturing processes. An engineer needs to choose the correct materials for the product they are working on.

Engineering materials can be divided into several categories. The main categories are **ferrous** and **non-ferrous metals**, and **thermosetting** and **thermoforming polymers**. A synthetic polymer is more commonly referred to as a plastic.

Identifying the correct type of material to use is very important. It will determine whether or not what you design and make fits the design brief and is usable by consumers.

ACTIVITY

Research and list as many ferrous and non-ferrous metals as you can. If possible, give an example of an engineered product made from each metal you list.

KEY TERMS

Ferrous metals contain iron. Ferrous metals include mild steel, cast iron and stainless steel.
Non-ferrous metals do not contain iron. Non-ferrous metals include aluminium, titanium, copper, silver and zinc.
Thermosetting polymers are materials that cannot be reshaped with the application of heat. Typical thermosetting polymers include phenol-formaldehyde, polyimides and polyurethane.
Thermoforming polymers are materials that can be reshaped with the application of heat. Typical thermoforming polymers include polyethylene, polypropylene and acrylic.

Ferrous metals

Ferrous metals contain iron (see Table 2.1). This means they have greater magnetic properties than other materials. Iron in its pure form is a soft, grey material that is difficult to machine as it gives a poor surface finish and does not cast or forge well. The addition of carbon changes and improves its properties, allowing the production of steel and cast iron.

Ferrous metals – except for stainless steel – are also very vulnerable to rust when exposed to water or moisture.

☐ **Table 2.1: Some types of ferrous metal**

Type	Properties	Composition (what it is made from)	Examples of use
Mild steel	<ul><li>Tough</li><li>Ductile</li><li>Magnetic</li><li>Malleable</li></ul>	<ul><li>Iron</li><li>0.1–0.3% carbon</li></ul>	<ul><li>Screws</li><li>Nails</li><li>Bolts</li></ul>
Cast iron	<ul><li>Hard</li><li>Brittle</li><li>Magnetic</li></ul>	<ul><li>Iron</li><li>2–4% carbon</li></ul>	<ul><li>Machine parts</li><li>Vices</li><li>Manhole covers</li></ul>
Stainless steel	<ul><li>Hard</li><li>Tough</li><li>Sometimes magnetic</li><li>Difficult to cut</li></ul>	<ul><li>Alloy</li><li>10.5% iron + carbon</li><li>10.5–18% chromium</li><li>8% nickel</li><li>8% manganese</li></ul>	<ul><li>Cutlery</li><li>Sinks</li><li>Medical equipment</li></ul>

KEY TERMS

Malleability is the ability of a material to be permanently deformed in all directions without breaking apart.
Ductility is the ability of a material to be deformed by bending, twisting or stretching. This ability increases in metals at higher temperatures.

Mild steel

Mild steel is an alloy of iron and carbon, and usually contains between 0.1% and 0.3% carbon. It is easy to machine and is the material you will probably use most regularly in a workshop. It is easy to work in a hot or cold state due to its **malleability** and **ductility**. Plain carbon steels are used in many situations, such as in girders, gates, machined parts, pressings and forgings.

Cast iron

Cast iron was a heavily used commodity prior to the discovery of steel. Often large structures, such as towers, were made from cast iron. The 158-metre-tall Blackpool Tower, built in 1894, is an example of a cast iron construction. However, over time, much of the original material has been replaced by steel girders. This is because steel is easier to work with – it is less brittle.

Stainless steel

Stainless steel is an **alloy** steel because, although it contains iron and carbon like mild steel, it also contains small amounts of chromium and nickel. The addition of the latter makes the material corrosion resistant (will not rust) and very tough. Stainless steel is used to make objects such as cutlery, kitchen sinks and washing machine drums. Generally, stainless steels are considered to be non-magnetic, although there are a limited number that can be magnetic.

KEY TERM

Alloys are mixtures of two or more metals that have improved properties and characteristics.

ACTIVITY

Look up the properties of medium carbon steel, high carbon steel and stainless steel. Write the properties in a table with headings the same as table 2.1, and then answer the questions below.

1 Which type of steel would you manufacture a chisel from? Why?

2 Why does the food preparation industry use stainless steel instead of a low carbon steel for equipment?

DID YOU KNOW?

Most ferrous metals can be identified with a magnet. They are magnetic.

CHECK MY LEARNING

In this section, you have learned how to identify ferrous and non-ferrous metals.

Working in small groups, select an engineered product and examine the different metals involved in its manufacture.

1 How many different metals can you recognise? List them.

2 Discuss your list and see if you can divide the metals into different categories. For example, iron is a ferrous metal.

Engineering materials: non-ferrous metals

GETTING STARTED

Non-ferrous metals are widely used in engineering throughout the electrical, aerospace and jewellery trades. It is important to understand their properties and uses and how to identify them.

Discuss why an engineered product made from a malleable material would be preferable to one that is not.

Non-ferrous metals

Non-ferrous metals are metals that do not contain iron. See Table 2.2 for examples of non-ferrous metals and some of their properties, composition and uses.

◘ **Table 2.2: Some types of non-ferrous metal**

Type	Properties	Composition (what it is made from)	Examples of use
Aluminium	• Corrosion resistant • Malleable • Ductile • Easily machined	• Pure metal	• Aircraft • Foil • Drinks cans
Copper	• Corrosion resistant • Malleable • Ductile • Tough • Easily machined • Good electrical conductor	• Pure metal	• Electrical wires • Pipes
Brass	• Casts well • Harder than copper • Easily machined	• Alloy • 65% copper • 35% zinc	• Plumbing fittings • Door fittings • Locks • Musical instruments

◘ **Why do you think these rotor blades for a gas turbine would be made from titanium?**

Titanium

Titanium is a strong, lightweight material that is highly resistant to corrosion. It is used in aircraft production and to make the shells for mobile phones. It is often alloyed with aluminium, vanadium or molybdenum to create very high-strength materials. Titanium is also used in the aerospace industry within jet engines, to provide **complex brackets** that are extremely strong.

Aluminium

Aluminium is a widely used non-ferrous metal. With a light silver or dull grey colour, it is malleable, resistant to corrosion and a good conductor of both heat and electricity. It is often alloyed with copper, silicon, iron, magnesium or manganese to enhance its properties, as in its pure form it has low tensile strength. Aluminium is used in the aircraft industry for fuselage and wing structures. Cookware is made from aluminium, as are drinks cans.

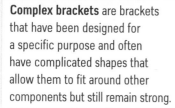

KEY TERM

Complex brackets are brackets that have been designed for a specific purpose and often have complicated shapes that allow them to fit around other components but still remain strong.

Copper

Copper has a reddish-orange colour and develops a green skin when the surface oxidises (corrodes). It is malleable, ductile, resistant to corrosion and a good conductor of both heat and electricity (see Figure 2.1). It is used in its almost pure form in the plumbing trade for water pipes and in the electrical trade as copper wire, and can also be used to manufacture cooking utensils. It can be alloyed with zinc to make brass.

◼ **Figure 2.1: Copper and other malleable materials can be formed into shape by hammering**

ACTIVITY

1 Why would a manufacturer choose brass rather than copper for the pins on a three-pin electrical plug?

2 What percentages of materials are used in the alloy composition of brass?

3 What are the major uses of the various brass alloys with different percentages of brass?

Silver

Silver is a bright metal that has the highest conductivity of electricity and heat of any known metal. It is classed as a precious metal, being often used to make jewellery and coinage. Within engineering, silver is used for electrical contacts and **conductors**. Solar cells and printed circuit boards (PCBs) use silver as a conductive link.

Zinc

Zinc has a dull grey appearance. Zinc is not corrosion resistant but it helps prevent steel from rusting. It provides electrochemical protection. **Galvanised** steel coated in zinc is used to coat building materials, as well as household items such as buckets. Zinc can also be used to **electroplate** nuts and bolts to provide a shiny corrosion-resistant surface.

KEY TERMS

Conductors are materials that transmit heat or electricity.
Galvanising is the process of providing a protective zinc coating to steel. Products tend to be hot-dipped to provide the coating.
Electroplating can be used to deposit a range of metals on the surface of another metal to provided corrosion resistance and/ or a decorative finish (for example, silver plating, chromium plating). .

ACTIVITY

Obtain some metallic engineered products.

1 See how many individual metals you can identify within your product.

2 Consider what alternative engineered products each metal could be used for.

CHECK MY LEARNING

There are many different non-ferrous metals. Answer the following questions to review what you have just learned.

1 How are non-ferrous metals different from ferrous metals?

2 Why does the food preparation industry use stainless steel instead of a low carbon steel?

Engineering materials: thermosetting polymers

GETTING STARTED

Polymers have a wide variety of uses in everyday life.

Consider your surroundings at home, at school and in leisure environments, and try to identify all of the products made from polymers. Can you explain why polymers have been used to make these items?

KEY TERM

Recycling is the process of converting waste material into other usable products.

◘ Polymer pellets – these are heated and formed into products

Polymers have revolutionised the world in the last 150 years. Look around you: where would we be without polymers? Most engineered products contain at least one component made from a polymer.

Synthetic polymers are essentially plastics and rubbers. Plastics come in many forms and shapes, from liquids and foams to solids. Plastics are oil-based materials that rely on the continual production of oil or the **recycling** of existing plastic products to maintain their production. Cross-linking is important in certain polymers. Cross-linking is where polymer chains are chemically bonded together in places. Because the polymer molecules cannot slide over each other so easily, this makes materials tougher and less flexible (see Figure 2.2 on page 85).

Polymers are now used in the production of:

- medicines
- household goods
- building materials.

Thermosetting polymers

Thermosetting polymers do not melt when heat is applied and cannot be re-formed by applying heat.

Once formed, thermosetting polymers cannot be altered. This means that they cannot be recycled and used again for another engineered product.

Phenol-formaldehyde

Phenol-formaldehyde is also known as phenolic resin. Phenolic resins are the original thermosetting polymer, first invented as Bakelite in 1907, from which telephone cases, plugs and sockets were first manufactured. These were moulded from a phenolic base with the addition of paper or fibreglass. Billiard balls are a typical product made from phenolic resin.

◘ Old-fashioned Bakelite telephone

Polyimides

Thermosetting polyimides are known for thermal stability, good chemical resistance and excellent mechanical properties. They are orange/yellow in colour and are used in the electronics industry for flexible cables, as an insulating film on magnet wire and for medical tubing. Due to their resistance to heat, the multi-layer insulation used on spacecraft is usually made of polyimide coated with thin layers of aluminium.

ACTIVITY

1 Look up the properties of melamine.
2 Why is it used for the bodies of electrical sockets?
3 Why is it used for kitchen utensils?

Polyurethane

Polyurethanes, also known as urethanes, can be produced as either rigid or flexible materials. Polyurethane is often produced as a foam, and can be found in engineered products such as footwear insoles or insulation foams. Polyurethanes are used for the manufacture of rigid foam insulation panels, durable wheels, roller coaster tyres and skateboard wheels, and low-density packing foams.

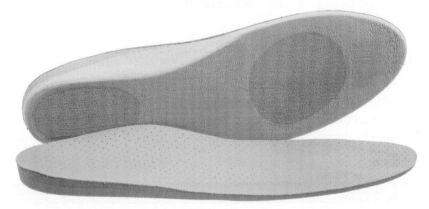

◘ Polyurethane midsoles in a sports shoe

ACTIVITY

Fill in the table below to summarise the different types of thermosetting polymer and their properties, forms and examples of use.

Thermosetting polymer	Properties	Forms	Examples of use
Phenol-formaldehyde			
Polyimides			
Polyurethane			

CHECK MY LEARNING

One of the main things to remember about thermosetting polymers is that they cannot be reused or recycled once they have been heated and cooled.

With this in mind, why are thermosetting polymers preferred for some engineered products?

Engineering materials: thermoforming polymers

Thermoforming polymers

The list of things polymers are used for is endless. However, it is becoming increasingly important for polymers to be recycled and to have less impact on the environment. Thermoforming polymers are different from thermosetting polymers in that they can be recycled. This means that they cause less damage to the environment because they can be reused when a product is no longer needed.

Thermoforming polymers can be softened by heating and often remoulded.

DID YOU KNOW?

Thermoforming polymers are sometimes referred to as thermoplastics.

Polyethylene

Polyethylene, also known as polythene, is the most common plastic in use in the world. It is a highly ductile material, which means that it can be stretched and **re-formed**. It is a tough and very flexible material that is used to manufacture plastic sacks and shopping bags. It is also very versatile, which means that it can be used to make lots of different things.

Polypropylene

Polypropylene is very similar to polythene, but it has more of a waxy feel. Because it is very difficult to glue to another polypropylene component with adhesive, it is normally **welded** instead. Polypropylene tends to be a tough and flexible polymer that can be used in many situations – automotive components, ropes, containers and the seats of school chairs.

KEY TERMS

Re-forming means changing something from one shape to another.
Welding means heating the surfaces of two objects to the point of melting and then joining them together.

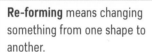

□ **Polypropylene school chair**

ACTIVITY

Examine a £5 note produced after September 2016. It feels waxy because the base material is polypropylene. Research why the £5 note was changed so that it could be made from this type of polymer.

Acrylic

Acrylic is a strong, rigid and **transparent polymer** that can be supplied as sheets, rods or tubes. It is often used to replace glass in greenhouses, lenses and visors, as it tends to be lighter and more resistant to breaking and shattering. It can be bent and blow moulded. Different colours can also be added.

KEY TERMS

A **transparent polymer** allows light to pass through it in such a way that objects behind it can be easily seen.
Blow moulding is a manufacturing process by which hollow plastic parts are formed.

DID YOU KNOW?

Polymers are long, intertwined chains of molecules. They are mainly made up of hydrogen and carbon atoms, and appear like long strands of spaghetti. Plastics and rubbers are classified as polymers. 'Poly' simply means 'many': a polymer is made from many monomers (individual molecules) joined together.

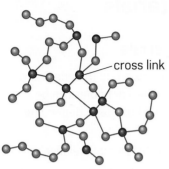
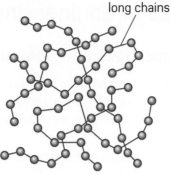

long chains

cross link

Thermosetting polymers   Thermoforming polymers

◻ **Figure 2.2: The structures of thermoforming and thermosetting polymers**

ACTIVITY

Obtain some acrylic sheeting. Using a line bender, bend the sheet through 90 degrees.

Once you have done this, heat the sheeting again and try to bend it back. Can you return it to a flat shape?

ACTIVITY

Research the industrial recycling and recovery process for the manufacture of products from recycled materials.

1 What different products can be manufactured in this way?

2 What initial polymers can be used?

ACTIVITY

Fill in the table below to summarise the different types of thermoforming polymer and their properties, forms and examples of use.

Thermoforming polymer	Properties	Forms	Examples of use
Polyethylene			
Polypropylene			
Acrylic			

CHECK MY LEARNING

Review the properties and identify as many uses as you can for these thermoforming polymers:

- polyethylene
- polypropylene
- acrylic.

Considering what you have learned about polymers, discuss the advantages and disadvantages of using thermoforming polymers to make a reusable plastic bottle.

Properties of engineering materials

General properties of engineering materials

Many polymers and metals are used for specific tasks. It is important to understand why certain materials are used for certain things. For example, car bodies can be made from different materials, such as steel, aluminium and fibreglass, depending on their primary use.

- Steel is used by the major motor manufacturers because it is strong, relatively cheap and easy to form.
- Aluminium is lightweight, dents easily, has good corrosion resistance and is often used in sportier cars and performance vehicles.
- Fibreglass has been tried in various vehicles because it is light, but it cracks under pressure and can be formed into large thin walled parts. It is ideal for rally cars and custom vehicles.

The most important properties of engineered products to remember are their strength, hardness and toughness.

Strength

The strength of a material is its ability to resist stress and strain.

- The **tensile** strength of a bar of material can be determined by the load that each cross-sectional area can carry before it fails or breaks.
- A metallic material will generally stretch and then break if **tension** is applied to each end. A polymer will generally stretch quite a lot before breaking.
- **Shear force** can be seen when metal scissors cut through paper.
- **Compression** tends to squash or shorten the material being subjected to that kind of force.

KEY TERMS

Tensile means something is capable of being stretched out.
Tension is the pulling force or forces on an object.
Shear force arises from forces that act in opposite directions.
Compressive strength is the ability of a material to resist a pushing force without being crushed.

Hardness

The hardness of a material is its **resistance to wear**, **abrasion** and **indentation**. Hard materials are brittle and difficult to cut. One of the hardest materials is diamond.

Although glass is hard, diamond is harder still. We know this because diamond is used to cut glass. While diamond is classed as one of the hardest known materials, it is not the toughest, because it fractures easily (allowing jewellers to work with it).

The high-speed steel cutting tools used in workshops are harder than mild steel. A hacksaw will saw through a mild steel or aluminium bar.

Toughness

A material that is tough is resistant to sudden impact or shock loading. Hammers are made to be tough so that they do not break or shatter on impact.

Most polymers are tough. They can withstand rough handling, which makes them suitable for a wide range of products.

Table 2.3 below shows the strength, hardness and toughness of some materials. Due to the different chemical structures within material groups, some of the properties can vary by as much as a factor of 30. See, for example, the hardness of aluminium (25 HB) and of hardened tool steel (750 HB).

◻ **Table 2.3: Summary of the strength, hardness and toughness of various metals**

Metal	Tensile strength (MPa)	Hardness (Brinell) (HB)	Toughness (kJ m^{-2})
Plain carbon steel	500	120	12
Cast iron	350	100	6
Stainless steel	750	200	10
Aluminium	95	25	10
Copper	230	35	30
Titanium	218	300	20
Silver	220	90	30
Zinc	200	35	15
Hardened tool steel	620	750	5

ACTIVITY

Using Table 2.3 and your own research, determine which metal is the:

1 toughest

2 strongest

3 hardest.

Give reasons for your choices.

CHECK MY LEARNING

All materials have properties that can be measured and compared with other materials.

In small groups, examine the chair on which you have been sitting.

1 Identify the toughest material in it.

2 Identify the strongest material in it.

3 Identify the hardest material in it.

Can you work out why the designer has selected these materials?

Characteristics of engineering materials

The characteristics of engineered materials can be categorised in the following ways:

- machinability is the ease with which a material can be cut and worked
- workability is the ease with which a metal or polymer can be reshaped
- durability is about the **lifespan** of a product or component.

Characteristics of metals

Machinability

In a workshop, you would normally use materials like mild or low carbon steel because they are easier to machine – they are alloyed with small amounts of lead to make them easier to machine or hacksaw. Similarly, aluminium is easy to machine as it is a free-cutting metal (it has a higher percentage of sulphur than carbon steel). Metals that have good machinability give a good surface finish, as long as the correct tooling, cutting speed and feeds are used.

Workability

Metals can be worked on using **cold working**; for example, copper has good workability at room temperature – it can be shaped into things like jewellery. Steel can also be worked cold, but it is better to work steel at red heat, in a forge, at temperatures above 750 degrees Celsius (**hot working**).

Durability

Durability is how much a product can withstand pressure or damage. If we were to build an engineered product as part of an assembly, it would not be a good idea to design one part to last 10 years, a second part to last 10 months and a third part to last 100 days. Designers need to be aware of a product's lifespan and ensure that all components used in the product will last or exceed that lifespan.

Some parts of a product are disposable. These are typically things like batteries, which can be recharged or replaced.

Some other important physical characteristics of metals are given in Table 2.4.

◻ **Table 2.4: Physical characteristics of metals**

Physical characteristic	Description
Conductivity	The ability of a metal to allow electricity to flow through it
Magnetism	The ability of a metal to attract or repel other metals that are magnetic
Density	How heavy something is relative to its volume; things feel heavier if they have a higher density

Characteristics of polymers

Machinability

Polymers are usually machined using cutting processes such as sawing, turning, drilling or die cutting. Polymers that have better machinability tend to be those that are rigid, such as ABS (acrylonitrile butadiene styrene) or nylon.

Workability

Polymers are very workable at relatively low temperatures. Polystyrene and many other polymers can be vacuum formed at approximately 135 degrees Celsius. Workability is also important for injection moulding, which is a technique often used when large numbers of the same moulded part are being made on an assembly line. For example, the temperature and pressure must be correct for the polymer to fill the mould.

Durability

The durability of polymers is difficult to calculate. Tests that replicate wear and tear are used to make comparison between different polymers. When selecting materials, designers need to consider how the product will need to perform in everyday life.

ACTIVITY

Think of something you have bought where one part did not last the product's lifespan – for example, the handle fell off a door. Which of the above material caracteristics was the prime reason for this?

ACTIVITY

Complete the table below. Research the listed materials and write down the characteristics of each.

Material	Machinability	Workability	Durability
Copper			
Low carbon steel			
Polystyrene			
Acrylic			

CHECK MY LEARNING

The characteristics of metals and polymers differ from material to material. Answer the following questions to recap what you have learned about these characteristics.

1 Write down definitions for the following terms: machinability; workability; durability.

2 Why is it important for an engineered product to be made from a durable metal or polymer?

Components: types and characteristics

A component is a part or element of a product.

Engineering is not simply about manufacturing components. Engineering can also involve buying components, which can be cheaper than making them yourself.

Many companies buy some items already made, and manufacture other items.

However, some assembly plants never manufacture anything. Instead, they just assemble different components into one product (for example, a finished car at the end of an assembly line).

Proprietary

Proprietary refers to a product for which somebody, usually a company, holds the rights to its design, so you are not allowed to copy it. The company alone makes and sells the product.

Within engineering, proprietary usually means a finished item that you would purchase from another supplier or stockist. Proprietary components are usually standard items such as:

- rivets
- nuts and bolts
- screws
- washers
- some electronic items such as **resistors**, **capacitors**, fuses, **diodes** and **LEDs**.

◪ **Can you list all the proprietary components shown in this picture?**

Product-specific

Many companies make their own components. Typically, these will be gears, shafts and flanges (components used to strengthen or attach other components to).

Within the electronics engineering industry, PCBs are an interesting case: some companies specialise in manufacturing PCBs which are then bought by computer, television and mobile phone manufacturers.

GETTING STARTED

Consider what a component of an engineered product could be. Make a list of all of the possibilities.

KEY TERMS

Resistors are electronic devices that restrict the flow of an electric current.

Capacitors are electronic devices that store electrical charge.

Diodes are electronic devices that can be used to allow electrical charge to flow in only one direction.

LED stands for 'light emitting diode' and produces light when a voltage is applied to it.

Characteristics of components

Many components have their own characteristics. Some of these refer to fixing methods, or fasteners. Some fixing methods are **permanent**, such as rivets or two components held together by welding or brazing. **Semi-permanent** fasteners are often nuts and bolts, items that can secure assemblies when tight but can be unfastened to release a component. Dowels are also used to locate components accurately.

When manufacturing components, it is important that sizes and dimensions are closely controlled. To ensure compatibility between all components, dimensions on an engineering drawing will usually have a tolerance. For example, the length of a shaft may be 150 mm plus or minus (±) 0.2 mm. This means that the maximum length that the shaft can be is 150.2 mm and the minimum it can be is 149.8 mm. This is important because if the shaft needs to fit a gearbox housing, the maximum size the gearbox housing can be is 149.7 mm, or it will not fit.

Surface roughness is created by machining a component, which leaves small hills and valleys on the surface.

Surface roughness can be checked with special gauges. If you have a set in your centre, check the surface textures of various items.

Value

All components and products have a value. Value can relate to cost or be of an ethical nature. For example, a bolt may cost 75p, but the company that sells it may have a value statement that it will recycle 75 per cent of its waste.

Engineering processes: shaping

Within engineering, many different manufacturing processes are employed. Some are very common, such as filing and hacksawing. Others are very specialised processes, such as additive machining (3D printing) of materials that are very difficult to produce, for example, low-volume, expensive components for the aerospace industry and F1 racing cars.

The most common processes you will come across in your school are listed below.

- **Shaping:** material is removed using tools, producing waste. Shaping methods are specific types of cutting process.
- **Cutting:** material is removed using tools, producing waste.
- **Joining:** materials are linked together – this can be permanent or semi-permanent.
- **Forming:** material is manipulated into a shape, producing little or no waste.

Shaping

Turning

Turning is a machining process in which parts are created by cutting away unwanted material from a larger piece. Material is cut away as the **workpiece** is rotated at high speeds.

Turning refers to shaping material on a manual or automatic **lathe**. The lathe grips the material within a **chuck**, and a cutting tool, which can be of various shapes and sizes, is used to produce cylindrical shapes.

Many commercially turned items are produced on a **CNC** lathe that can be programmed to produce and then accurately reproduce particularly complex shapes time after time.

ACTIVITY

Look at a simple component part, such as a bolt.

1. Write a plan to machine the component part, listing the processes you would use in the correct order.
2. Select a material to use and explain why you have chosen that material.
3. Research methods that can be used to cut the screw thread of the bolt.

LINK IT UP

A lathe is very versatile and can produce many different kinds of shape. As well as turning, it can also be used for drilling, but in drilling it is the drill that spins while the workpiece is stationary. You will learn about drilling on page 94.

Milling

There are two types of milling machine – horizontal and vertical. Both are used to machine flat surfaces. They can also be used to create slots and **recesses**. A milling machine does this by using a rotating cutter with multiple teeth that removes material from the surface of the workpiece.

Vertical milling machines differ from horizontal ones in that they are fitted with cutters that have multiple cutting edges, and most feature CNC systems. Many commercially milled items are produced on a CNC milling machine – particularly complex shapes, which can be programmed and then accurately repeated time after time.

KEY TERM

Recesses are internal grooves, also known as pocket cuts.

DID YOU KNOW?

To program a CNC lathe or milling machine, it is important to understand how a conventional lathe or milling machine works so that you can calculate feeds and speeds and optimum cutting paths.

CHECK MY LEARNING

Shaping is a particular type of cutting.

Describe the differences between turning and milling. What are the similarities between them?

◨ **Setting up a tool on centre lathe: tool is re-set and diameter turned down**

Engineering processes: cutting

KEY TERMS

A **blind hole** is a hole that does not break through to the other side of the workpiece.

A **pilot hole** is a small hole drilled ahead of a full-sized hole as a guide.

Cutting

Cutting processes are used either to divide materials into more than one piece, or to get rid of unwanted material. Although this can be done manually, many of the methods are automated.

Drilling

Drilling is a cutting process that is often performed as a machining operation to produce various sizes of hole. Holes are cut using a drill bit as it rotates in the workpiece. Through holes go all the way through the material. **Blind holes** only go part way through.

Listed below are the important things you need to remember when you are drilling.

- Firstly, mark up the workpiece and use a centre punch to mark the exact position of the hole.
- If you need to drill a large-diameter hole, drill a small **pilot hole** first.
- If you are drilling through a thin piece of material, clamp a piece of wood under it first.

The correct speed (revolutions per minute – RPM or rpm) of a drill can be calculated using the formula:

$$N = \frac{1000 \times S}{\pi d}$$

(where N is the RPM, S is the cutting speed in metres per minute and d is the diameter in metres of the workpiece on a lathe or of the drill in a drilling operation).

ACTIVITY

A low carbon steel bar is turned on a lathe.

Calculate the correct RPM if the cutting speed is 27 metres per minute and the diameter is 25 mm.

KEY TERM

Teeth are the grooves on engineering tools.

Sawing

Sawing is a cutting operation that can be done by hand with a junior hacksaw or a hacksaw or on a machine with a power hacksaw. It may also be used to cut a metal bar to the correct length or to cut out a slot or groove. Hacksaw blades come with different numbers of **teeth** per inch (TPI): 14, 18, 24 and 32 TPI.

When using a hacksaw for sawing, the following things should be remembered:

- Ensure that you always have a minimum of three teeth on the material to be cut.
- 14 TPI should be used to cut softer materials such as aluminium.
- 18 TPI is the most commonly used hacksaw blade, and should be used generally.
- 24 TPI should be used for cutting materials that are thin.
- 32 TPI should be used for fine cuts, such as pipe or tubing.

Filing

Files come in many shapes and sizes, but the most common files are flat or half round files. Flat files are used for removing excess material or smoothing faces, and for creating flat faces. Files, like hacksaws, come in a range of lengths and numbers of teeth per inch and are referred to as rough, bastard, second cut, smooth and dead smooth. A rough file is used on surfaces that need a lot of material removed, and where it is impractical to saw the excess material off to finish components accurately to a good surface finish.

Shearing

Shearing is another word for mechanical cutting, or cutting in its simplest form (see Figure 2.3). An example would be the way in which a pair of scissors cuts paper.

Shearing can be done with tin snips, which have straight or curved blades. These can be used to cut very detailed and intricate shapes from very thin materials.

Shearing can also be achieved with hand-operated, bench-mounted shears and with power guillotine shears – these can cut plates that are thicker.

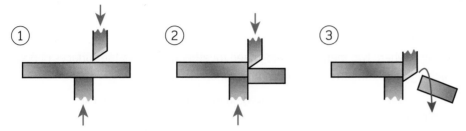

☐ Figure 2.3: The shearing action of mechanical cutting

ACTIVITY

Practise your shearing skills.

1 Find a piece of thin steel.
2 Mark a centre point and draw a circle with a diameter of 100 mm.
3 Cut around the circle with tin snips.
4 How accurate is your cutting? With a partner, review each other's results and discuss how well you think you have done.

Laser cutting

Laser cutting is a technique that uses lasers to cut materials. It works by directing a laser beam onto the surface of the material being cut.

An advantage of using laser cutting is that it produces a very good edge finish and there is very little distortion by the heat from the laser because the beam width is very narrow.

DID YOU KNOW?

Thermal cutting involving the use of heat is essentially a melting process.

ACTIVITY

Obtain three different files and three different hacksaws from the workshop, then fill in the table below.

File or hacksaw	What type of file or hacksaw is it?	How many teeth does it have?	In which circumstances would you use this file or hacksaw?
File #1			
File #2			
File #3			
Hacksaw #1			
Hacksaw #2			
Hacksaw #3			

CHECK MY LEARNING

You have learned about one of the main engineering processes, cutting.

Give definitions for all of the different types of cutting you have learned about.

Engineering processes: joining

Joining

There are two different types of joining process – permanent and non-permanent.

Permanent joining includes:

- welding
- bonding.

Non-permanent joining includes:

- fastening.

Welding

Welding is where two metal parts are joined together by heating the surfaces of both to melting point with an oxyacetylene torch or an electric arc.

This process does not work if there is oxygen present, so air must be excluded from the heated area.

ACTIVITY

Research the different methods used to prevent oxidation in the welding process.

Bonding

Bonding means adhering two surfaces together, and can be done in various different ways.

Adhesives (like glue) can be used. There are slow-curing adhesives, such as epoxy resins, or very fast adhesives, such as super glue.

Electrical and electronic items such as resistors are often soldered together at low temperatures. Brazing is used at higher temperatures, by melting a filler rod into the joint. For both soldering and brazing, the filler rod melts at a lower temperature than the parent metal; it is only in welding that the parent metal and any filler both melt.

Adhesives

Slow-curing adhesives need time to harden; fast-curing adhesives work instantly. Both kinds can be used on nearly all types of material, but fast-curing adhesives (like super glue) have more industrial uses.

DID YOU KNOW?

Fast-curing adhesives, such as super glue, are also known as cyanoacrylates.

Brazing

Brazing is different from welding in that the materials being joined are not melted and fused directly. Brazing is used to join mild steel components. An alloy of copper and zinc is melted at high temperatures and joins the steel by flowing into the joint.

Soldering

Soldering works in the same way as brazing, but at a lower temperature.

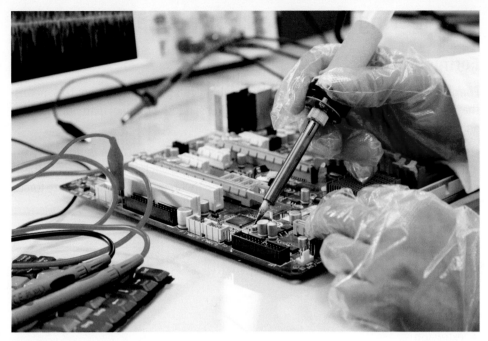

◧ **Soldering electronic parts**

Fastening

Fastenings are non-permanent ways of joining two materials. Types of fastening include:

- screwed fastenings, like nuts, bolts, washers and screws
- pins and dowels.

One of the main things to remember when fitting a screwed fastener is how tight it should be and whether this tightness will be affected by any vibration.

Pins and dowels are used to hold parts together when very accurate locations are needed. For example, in a gearbox in a car, many parts need to be aligned exactly with others for the gearbox to work correctly. This is done using dowels, which maintain alignment, and bolts, which hold the parts together.

◧ **Different types of fastening**

ACTIVITY

Research the best joining techniques to use in the following examples. Give reasons for your answers.

1 Mounting electronic components on a PCB.
2 Joining two mild steel pipes.
3 Joining different component parts of a bike frame.

CHECK MY LEARNING

There are many different types of joining process within engineering.

With a partner create a short presentation on the different ways in which metals can be joined. Use real-life examples to explain each process.

Engineering processes: forming polymers

Forming

Forming is when materials are reshaped through mechanical deformation. This means that no material is added or removed in the process, but the original material changes shape.

Forming is a very cost-effective way of engineering a material because there is very little waste. Many engineering components are produced via forming processes. This is often done at high temperatures using moulding techniques or applying large forces to reshape materials.

Forming can be used on both polymers and metals.

Polymers can be formed by:

- extrusion
- injection moulding.

Metals can be formed by:

- extrusion
- casting
- forging
- folding
- bending.

Nearly all products made from polymers are produced by a forming process because it is so quick and cost-effective. It also gives a very good finish without a lot of manual work being needed – extrusion and moulding are both automated processes.

Extruding

Extrusion involves heating plastic granules until they are in a liquid state, and then forcing them through a **die** (see Figure 2.4). Think of it as like squeezing toothpaste from a tube.

The plastic leaving the die will be soft, and after passing through a cooling chamber, it is gently pulled by rollers and then cut to the correct lengths.

Although extrusion is most commonly used to form polymers, it can also be used on metals. The process is much the same, except that no heat is involved.

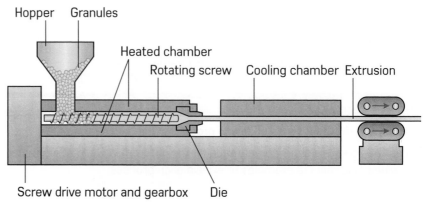

■ Figure 2.4: The extrusion process

Injection moulding

Injection moulding is the process of filling a preformed shape with liquid polymers (see Figure 2.5). The liquid is forced into the mould using pressure, and the liquid then cools to become solid and adopts the shape of the mould. Many polymers are moulded to create items such as calculator cases, mobile phone cases and kettle bodies.

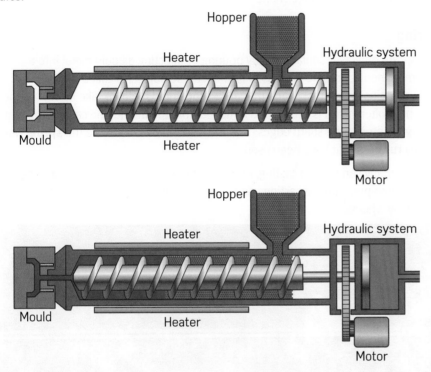

 Figure 2.5: The process of injection moulding

ACTIVITY

Injection moulding can be used for many different engineering components, and it is a process that is suitable for use with a wide range of polymers.

Carry out some research to find examples of components that have been manufactured using injection moulding, and then answer the following questions.

1 What is the component, and what is its function?

2 What type of polymer is the component made of, and why?

3 What are the advantages of using injection moulding to produce the component?

CHECK MY LEARNING

Extrusion and moulding are processes used to form polymers.

1 Research the types of things made using extrusion and moulding techniques.

2 Using what you have learned in this lesson and your own research, write a step-by-step process describing how you would form something using both extrusion and moulding techniques.

Engineering processes: forming metals

KEY TERMS

Fettling means trimming or cleaning the edges of a metal casting.

Sprue is the hole that molten metal is poured into when casting. When the casting solidifies, the sprue needs to be removed.

Risers occur where excess metal from the moulding escapes from the casting box. They will also solidify, and so need to be removed at the end of the process.

Runners are used to allow metal to flow from one moulding to another so that multiple parts can be cast at the same time.

Most metals are ductile. Because of this, they can be plastically deformed by applying force to them.

Plastic deformation means that when a big enough force is applied to a material, it will cause the material to change shape.

Casting

Castings are objects manufactured by pouring or injecting a liquid metal into a preformed mould, and the process of forming these objects is called casting. The mould contains an internal shape that allows the liquid metal to take its cast shape. Once the molten metal is cooled and removed from the mould, the casting will require **fettling** to remove the sharp edges. This will also remove items like the **sprue**, **risers** and any **runners** that have been used.

There are many variables in casting, from floor moulding to produce flat drainage grates, to low-pressure die casting used for parts that require close tolerances, such as car alloy wheels.

◨ Casting

Forging

Forging has been used for centuries as a hand process, using an anvil, hammer, tongs and various formers. This historically was used to make weapons, hand tools and horseshoes.

Forging is a slow, highly skilled job. You may have used a forge to shape a screwdriver bit or a chisel. When used to make commercial products, forging is a similar process to regular forging but on a larger scale, using large hammer blows or a power press to squeeze the component into shape.

Press forming

Press forming normally involves using a press brake (see Figure 2.6). This is a large machine used to bend sheet metal. The bends are formed by pressing the sheet metal or plating between a punch and a die. A piece of sheet steel is positioned over the die block, which then presses the sheet to form the required shape.

◻ A press formed component

◻ Figure 2.6: Vee block and blade tooling used to form bends on a press brake.

Bending

Bending of metal can be done by hand using a hammer and a vice. However, this way of working is not very accurate. For a more precise finish, a press brake is used.

To make a 90 degree bend in a small piece of mild steel would require overbending by a few degrees. When marking out before forming a bend, extra length (or bend allowance) should be added to the material.

In your workshop, you may have a manual sheet metal folder. The bending capacity of press brakes and metal folders is about 120 degrees, depending on the thickness of the sheet.

ACTIVITY

Research folding and bending processes in the manufacture of common everyday items. These could include tool boxes, shelf brackets, trunking and filing cabinets.

Make notes and sketches to illustrate the processes.

CHECK MY LEARNING

Forming processes for polymers and metals have some similarities and some differences.

List any similarities and differences you can think of between the forming processes for metals and those for polymers, giving specific examples where you can.

Learning aim A: assessment practice

How you will be assessed

In Component 2 you will be assessed by completing a series of internally set assignments.

When completing the assignment covering Learning Aim A, you will need to show that you understand the different materials, components and processes used in the manufacture of an engineered product.

This will include demonstrating a detailed understanding of:

- engineering materials and their uses
- the properties of different engineering materials, and their importance when selecting materials for different purposes
- the types and characteristics of components used in engineered products.

CHECKPOINT

Strengthen

- Note down examples of materials that fall into each of the main material categories.
- Explain the differences between strength, hardness and toughness.
- List the engineering processes commonly used to form polymers components.

Challenge

- Explain the difference between a product specific and a proprietary component.
- Describe two advantages of using proprietary components for engineering products.
- Write descriptions of five processes commonly used to manufacture metal components, using annotated sketches to support your text.

ASSESSMENT ACTIVITY | LEARNING AIM | A

Description

In this assignment, you will be asked to investigate engineering materials, components and processes and how they interrelate.

Example tasks

Select a product that you are familiar with and is supported by technical information including exploded assembly drawings (often available online from product manufacturers and used during disassembly, repair and maintenance activities). Examples of a suitable product might be a: skateboard, roller skate, bicycle brake assembly, industrial light fitting, radio controlled car suspension assembly, or a cyclist's folding multi-tool.

Once you have selected a product, you should then:

- identify all of the components and annotate the assembly drawing
- make a list of the components
- consider for each whether it is a proprietary component or a product specific component
- identify the material that each component is made from.

Having identified these components and materials carry out an investigation, using Internet research, to find out about:

- the availability of the proprietary components, what they do and how they work
- the properties of the materials you have identified
- the processes used to make each product specific component you have identified.

During your investigation, ensure you bring together all of the information and review it to form a conclusion that includes why each material is used, why each proprietary component is used and why each process is used to make product specific components.

You should draw on evidence you have found, including strengths and weaknesses of each and alternatives that could be used. You should gather all of your work into a small folder containing notes and images to present as evidence for assessment.

Evidence

Evidence could include:

- annotated assembly and detailed drawings
- a list of components, materials and processes used
- research notes
- notes to evaluate the materials, components and processes you have researched
- images in support of your work.

TIPS

To gain a distinction, you will need to present detailed evaluations of why particular materials and processes were chosen. An evaluation should include a discussion of the advantages and disadvantages of several alternatives and a justified conclusion explaining which option would be best and why.

TAKE IT FURTHER

Investigate how the strength, hardness and toughness of materials are measured and the equipment used to test these properties.

Practical engineering skills 1

Within engineering it is important to be able to examine components, products and assemblies and understand how they are produced or made. Investigations involving disassembly are very useful here.

For this learning aim, you need to:

- select an engineered product and investigate its purpose and function
- use hand tools and work safely to dismantle the product
- lay out the parts, label them and identify the function of each one
- measure the dimensions of each part that has been machined/formed, and record these on simple sketches
- write a product design specification (PDS) for the product (see Figure 2.7).

Product Design Specification
Revision Date:
Team Leader:
_____
_____

Team Members:
_____
_____

Product Title: _____

1. Purpose
_____
_____
_____
_____

2. Features
_____
_____
_____
_____
_____
_____

3. Competition
_____
_____
_____

4. Intended market
_____
_____
_____

5. Performance requirements
_____
_____
_____

6. Life-cycle
_____
_____

7. Other factors
_____
_____
_____
_____

▣ **Figure 2.7: A template for a product design specification (PDS)**

Observing and recording skills

As you move through the practical work in Learning aims B and C, start a logbook (see Figure 2.8) or diary and remember to keep it up to date.

- Record your decisions and your reasons for making them.
- Make notes of things that went well or things that did not go so well.
- Record procedures for disassembly.
- Record the tools used.
- Record labels for components.
- List items that will need to be replaced.
- Make notes about the materials used.
- Make notes about safety precautions and rules.
- Take photographs.

You must be able to examine certain features of an engineered product and determine various things from your observations, such as features and purpose.

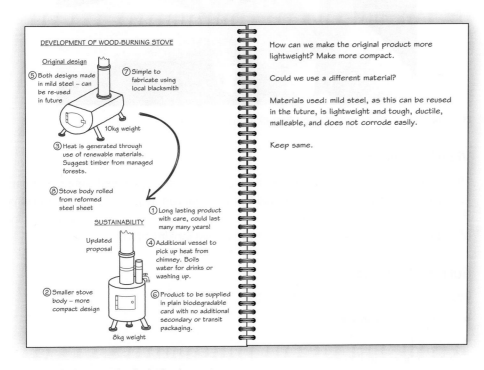

■ **Figure 2.8: An example of a logbook**

ACTIVITY

Make a list of all the tools and equipment you have been shown how to use safely.

For each item, write down what it is used for and any safety precautions you need to follow.

Then, make a list of the tools and equipment in your engineering workshop that you do not know the purpose of or how to use. Carry out some research to find out what these tools are for.

CHECK MY LEARNING

Discuss with a partner the advantages of keeping a logbook of all of the engineering activities that you complete on your course.

Practical engineering skills 2

GETTING STARTED

With a partner, think about all the pieces of information that you would need to know about an engineering component to be able to make it. How would you find out this information?

Practical engineering skills, such as observing and examining the features of different engineered component parts, are very important. In this lesson you will look at an example that goes through everything you should be examining when observing and recording the features of an engineered product. The example that we are going to look at is a bolt.

Example: consider a bolt

◻ What can you observe about a bolt like this?

Visual features

The first step in recording the purpose and function of an engineered component part is to use your eyes to identify any visual features that can help you to understand what the part is intended for. This bolt is made of metal and is small (though the actual type of metal, length and mass cannot be known by just looking at it).

Surface features

What are the surface features of the bolt?

- It has a screw **thread**.
- It has a plain diameter.
- It has a hexagonal head.
- There are letters and numbers on the top of the head.
- It has a bright surface finish.

KEY TERM

A **thread** is a raised structure on a screw or bolt that follows a helical path and allows parts to be joined together.

Mass

Examining the bolt more closely, can you estimate its mass? You could use scales to weigh it to get an accurate reading.

What does the mass of a bolt tell us about it? If you know its mass, and you thought it was reasonably heavy, you could compare it to a similar piece of aluminium or steel or brass, and this could identify the material for you. If you know the mass and volume, then the mass divided by the volume will give you the density of the bolt. You could look up the density in a table similar to Table 2.5, or search online to identify the exact material.

LINK IT UP

Mass is discussed further on page 114.

■ Table 2.5: Densities of some common materials

Material	Density (kg m⁻³)
Air	1.29
Aluminium	2691
Copper (cast)	8680
Glass	3140
Cast iron	7209
Rubber	1520
Steel	7769
Water	1000

Colour

What does the colour of the bolt tell us?

The bolt is a bright, silvery colour, and therefore it is clear that it has been plated. The standard process for plating bolts is zinc **plating**, and so we can safely say that it is zinc-plated. It has been zinc-plated for protection against **rusting**, and also to give it a nice appearance when holding parts together – you would not want to purchase a bolt for your bicycle that was rusty!

Degradation

Degradation is the process by which the condition of a product worsens over time. Does the bolt show any signs of rusting or damage? If not, we can presume that it is new or has had very little use.

Identification marks

Are there any identification marks apparent on the bolt?

The head has some letters and numbers on it. The letters indicate who the manufacturer is. The numbers specify the grade of bolt. If it shows 8.8 (as in the photo on page 106) then you know two things:

1 It is a metric bolt.

2 8.8 is the grade of a standard, high-tensile bolt.

KEY TERMS

Plating is a thin coating of gold, silver or other metal.

Rusting is when a metal becomes covered in a reddish-brown, flaking coating of iron oxide. Rusting affects iron and steel.

ACTIVITY

Take an engineered product (such as a hand tool from your engineering workshop or an item that your teacher has provided) and then observe and record its various parameters:

1 visual features

2 surface features

3 mass

4 colour

5 degradation

6 identification marks.

For your notes, it might be useful to take a picture of the product.

CHECK MY LEARNING

Compare your observations of the product that you have examined with those of another student who observed the same or a similar item. What similarities or differences are there in your descriptions and observations?

Practical engineering skills 3

Measurement skills

It is important to be able to measure accurately. To do this, you need to use the correct tool with the correct method. Some engineering products are measured to 0.0001 mm – there are some very fine measurements used in industry. If things are not measured accurately, it could compromise the quality of a product or how well it works.

Again, a bolt will be used as an example.

Measuring diameter

Diameter is the measurement through the centre of a circle from edge to edge.

To help identify the bolt on page 106, you need to know its exact size. A good place to start is to measure the diameter, because this will help to identify the thread size. If the diameter is 12 mm, then the bolt is a 12 mm threaded bolt.

You can find the diameter by using a special measuring instrument, such as a micrometer, Vernier callipers or callipers and rule. The type of measuring instrument you would need to use depends on the accuracy and precision that you require. A micrometer should accurately measure to 0.01 mm; Vernier callipers will accurately measure to 0.02 mm, and a set of callipers and rule should measure to about 0.4 mm. The accuracy of the measurements obviously depends on the skill of the person using the measuring instruments.

Measuring linear dimensions

Linear dimensions are often easier to measure than diameters. Linear dimensions refer to the length, width and thickness of an object or component.

Looking at the bolt, it would be good to know its overall length, the length of the thread and the across flats (AF) dimension. These factors, along with the thread size, tell us the information needed to purchase this bolt. The AF size is required because that tells us the spanner size needed to fasten or unfasten the bolt. These dimensions can all be measured easily with a rule.

ACTIVITY

Can you order a bolt or a nut via the internet? List some of the information that would be required to place an accurate order.

Use of comparative techniques

If you have a box of bolts, it is straightforward to sort them by spanner size. Table 2.6 shows how measuring the AF size will give you the diameter.

Table 2.6: Bolt diameters and AF sizes

Bolt AF size	Bolt diameter
8 mm	5 mm
10 mm	6 mm
3 mm	8 mm
18 mm	12 mm

Knowledge of component values

Bolts cannot be sorted by colour coding, but many components can. A resistor is a good example of a component that can be colour-coded (see Figure 2.9).

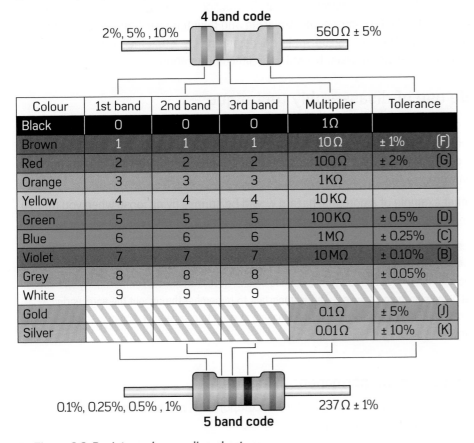

Colour	1st band	2nd band	3rd band	Multiplier	Tolerance	
Black	0	0	0	1Ω		
Brown	1	1	1	10Ω	± 1%	(F)
Red	2	2	2	100Ω	± 2%	(G)
Orange	3	3	3	1KΩ		
Yellow	4	4	4	10KΩ		
Green	5	5	5	100KΩ	± 0.5%	(D)
Blue	6	6	6	1MΩ	± 0.25%	(C)
Violet	7	7	7	10MΩ	± 0.10%	(B)
Grey	8	8	8		± 0.05%	
White	9	9	9			
Gold				0.1Ω	± 5%	(J)
Silver				0.01Ω	± 10%	(K)

◘ **Figure 2.9: Resistor colour-coding chart**

Colour-coding charts are not difficult to read, but if you are unsure, many electronic suppliers produce a circular colour wheel to set the colour values, and this will then tell you the value of the resistor.

Justification and reasoning

Appraisal and interpretation skills are important when it comes to making decisions about whether a component part of an engineering assembly needs to be replaced. You will need to consider the condition of the component – for example, is it damaged in some way? You will then need to interpret any information you have to identify the replacement part that will be needed. You should be able to give reasons for deciding to replace a component, some of which we will look at in a later lesson.

ACTIVITY

Working in pairs, obtain a selection of nuts and bolts and measure their:

a) length

b) diameter

c) thread size.

1 Record your results and compare them with those of your partner.

2 Swap your items with another group and repeat the exercise.

3 Compare all of the measurements across the whole class. What differences are there? Why might that be?

CHECK MY LEARNING

Why do you think bolts and nuts have standard AF features?

Revisit the initial evaluation of practical engineering skills from the first lesson of Learning aim B, and re-evaluate your own strengths and areas needing development.

Disassembly techniques

GETTING STARTED

There are right and wrong ways to disassemble an engineering product or component part of a product.

Working in pairs, think about what the term disassembly means and write out a definition of the word.

Disassembly is a skill that requires you to be organised: it involves numbering and cleaning parts as well as laying them out. The reasons for disassembly include the replacement of faulty components, servicing and maintenance. Remember, if you have dismantled something, it usually needs putting back together. You need to be organised, otherwise reassembly will be a difficult operation.

Safe use of disassembly techniques

If a component part of an engineered product is not disassembled correctly, it can potentially be very dangerous. For example, oil can spill or spurt out under pressure. This could cause injury if the correct personal protective equipment (PPE) has not been worn.

Another example of a potential hazard would be springs flying loose when you undo a plate.

DID YOU KNOW?

A golden rule to maintain safety in a working area is: never use any tool or machinery without first being shown how to use it. This is important to remember throughout the engineering process, but it is especially crucial when looking at ways to disassemble engineered products or component parts.

Removal of semi-permanent fixings

There are many ways of joining materials, components, products and assemblies. There are two general types of fixing method:

- permanent fixings
- semi-permanent fixings (sometimes called temporary fixings).

The difference between them is that semi-permanent fixings can be taken apart and reassembled. These are the fixings that the information on disassembly techniques will apply to.

Permanent fixing methods include welding, brazing, soldering, riveting and the use of adhesives.

LINK IT UP

Permanent and semi-permanent fixings are also discussed on page 91.

Semi-permanent fixings include nuts and bolts, screws, double-sided tape and knock-down kits (such as items found in self-build furniture), plastic blocks and screws and cams and locks.

Semi-permanent fixings can be removed and refastened without destroying the joint.

Parts removal and layout

Disassembly should be an orderly process. It is no use simply starting to pull things apart or undo fastenings, as items will get lost or damaged, and when you come to reassemble the component you will not know where the various items belong.

Before starting to disassemble, take some photographs or draw some sketches of the assembled product or component – obtain an assembly drawing if you can. These steps will help you to reassemble the parts in the correct order or position.

As you disassemble, clean all the parts as you remove them, then lay them all out on a piece of paper or cloth, preferably numbering them. If you have unscrewed something, number the fastening as well as the hole it came out of. If that is not possible, take a photo with a numbered card next to it.

Use a set of good-quality tools for your disassembly work; ensure screwdrivers and spanners fit as they should, and use the correct size and type of screwdriver for each screw. Using a magnetised screwdriver to remove small screws will help prevent you from dropping them. When you drop a small screw, you will realise how valuable it is if you can't find it again!

Be organised: use small plastic boxes or small metal trays to keep common parts together.

Replacement of non-reusable consumables or fixings

Not all consumables can be reused when you reassemble a product. For example, if you remove an 'oil seal' or an 'O' ring, it is always better to fit a new one rather than reuse the old one, since the old one could have become damaged when it was removed and might cause oil to leak.

If you remove an oil filter, or any other component that has a limited lifespan, you should replace it with a new one. Think before you start to disassemble, 'Have I got all the replacement parts that I am likely to need?'

Certain nuts have a ring of plastic at the top of the thread. These are called nyloc nuts, and the plastic insert deforms to lock the nut onto the screw. If you take a nyloc nut off an assembly, you should replace it with a new one if the plastic insert is damaged, or else it will not self-lock properly when it is put back.

When you dismantle a product, you need to remember that some manufacturers use locking substances to stop certain nuts and bolts from being removed or coming loose. Other manufacturers use screws and bolts with special heads to prevent assemblies being disassembled easily; often Torx drivers are needed to remove these screws.

◻ **Nyloc nut**

DID YOU KNOW?

Check the lifespan of all components in an assembly if you can. For example, a bearing may need changing after 500 hours of working life.

ACTIVITY

Obtain a small, engineered assembly. Working in small groups, answer the following questions.

1 Identify the items you need to store the various parts when you remove them.

2 List the tools you will need to disassemble the product.

3 Identify the semi-permanent and permanent fixings.

4 Identify which parts look difficult to remove.

CHECK MY LEARNING

In this section, you have learned about the disassembly of engineered products and component parts. Based on what you have learned, list the steps you would need to follow when removing parts from an engineered assembly and laying them out.

Disassembly tools

GETTING STARTED

Disassembly is an important part of investigating an engineering project. If you use the wrong tool to disassemble something, you could damage the component part.

Research and then list the organisational steps and safety considerations when using disassembly techniques.

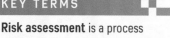

KEY TERMS

Risk assessment is a process used to document that all hazards have been considered and appropriate measures put in place to deal with them.

Drifts are tools used for enlarging holes.

Disassembly is a skill that requires a good knowledge of products, materials and processes. Some items cannot simply be replaced with the original part – they must be new. Safety and organisation are very important in the disassembly process. Remember to always perform a **risk assessment** and never put yourself or your colleagues in danger.

LINK IT UP

Risk assessments are also covered on pages 9, 116 and 131.

The different types of tools for disassembly

The following tools are commonly used in disassembly:

- spanners
- torque wrenches
- **drifts**
- screwdrivers.

Safe use of tools and equipment – disassembly/reassembly tools with settings

Within engineering, safety is vitally important in every action you take. The correct PPE is fundamental to your safety.

Personal protective equipment (PPE)

The correct PPE can be any combination of:

- overalls
- safety glasses
- safety shoes or boots
- protective face mask
- barrier cream
- welding helmet or goggles
- high-visibility clothing
- safety harnesses.

What PPE is needed depends on what you are doing and the risks involved. A risk assessment of a task can help you to determine what protective equipment you will need.

Correct ways to hold and use tools

All good engineers will hold the tools for a job correctly and use them appropriately. For example, a screwdriver is not a lever or a paint scraper: it is used to fasten and unfasten screws.

Many people make the mistake of using an incorrect type of screwdriver for a particular screw and strip the screw head, making the screw nearly impossible to remove without drilling it out. Alternatively, they might damage the blade of the screwdriver.

DID YOU KNOW?

It is not sensible to try to take a complex item apart if you have not referred to the manufacturer's service manual.

Spanners

◻ **Open-ended spanner**

Open-ended spanners are double-ended, with two different-sized ends. Note that the spanner in the photograph is for a 19 mm and a 17 mm bolt or nut. To use this spanner correctly and safely, you must rotate the spanner by pulling on the **shank**. If that cannot be achieved due to restrictions, there is no choice but to push the spanner using the palm of your hand while keeping your hand open. The shank is angled away from the head, and this allows the spanner to be rotated on its axis, enabling you to turn the spanner from two different angles in limited spaces.

Spanners come in many sizes and forms, including open-ended, ring and adjustable spanners. There are also specialist spanners and ratchet spanners.

Some bolts or nuts or other fasteners need to be fastened to a specific torque (turning force). Cylinder head nuts are fastened in a specific order and to a certain torque, while car wheel nuts are tightened to a specific torque. This is carried out with a torque wrench. The wrench will 'click' or 'break' and will not allow any more turns of the bolt or nut when the correct torque is reached.

KEY TERM

A **shank** is the shaft of a tool.

ACTIVITY

List examples of times where you would use a torque wrench.

All of the above tools can be used in a disassembly and reassembly process. There are many other engineering tools used in assembly and disassembly – such as Allen keys, hammers, punches, hacksaws, pliers, chisels and multimeters.

ACTIVITY

Obtain a small, engineered assembly and, working in small groups, follow these steps.
1 Identify the PPE you will need.
2 List the tools you will need.
3 List the documents you would need to refer to when disassembling and reassembling the product.
4 List the photographs you would take.
5 Sketch how you would lay out the various components.
6 Identify the hazards.
7 Identify the risks.
8 Check with your teacher if it is safe to start dismantling.

CHECK MY LEARNING

The type of tool you use during disassembly is very important. What types of PPE might you need for carrying out disassembly tasks?

Product design specification (PDS)

It is likely that you have seen **product design specification (PDS)**, probably without recognising it.

A PDS determines the requirements of a product or assembly that a customer may want to see. You will need to create the technical specification for your engineered assembly, component or product – the PDS. If you purchase a new electrical appliance, you will find a technical specification in the instruction manual or as a separate document. This will have been created from the PDS.

Look at the specification for an electronic device such as a calculator. It will give you information about the size, battery, performance and function of the device, as well as any standards and legislation associated with that type of product. All of this information has originated from the PDS.

Things you need to consider

A properly drawn up PDS will:

- set out all parameters for the assembly of the engineered product: size and mass, product life and reliability, performance/function/service requirements, economic and making considerations, and implications of standards and legislation
- provide a base for all of the drawings
- provide a base for design, manufacture, service and meeting regulations
- determine what the product, service or process will do.

A PDS is a live document and will be changed and updated many times. You should expect your PDS to grow as you work your way through designing your product. To get the most from your PDS, you should start simply, with just the basic information. Your PDS will grow as you develop your product design.

A PDS must contain basic information so that the design team can use it to develop ideas and produce drawings. What do you think are the basic requirements?

Size and mass

A PDS must specify the maximum and minimum sizes as well as the mass of a product. Size can be given by the maximum and minimum dimensions. In a PDS, you must ensure that measurements are accurate – this means using the correct measuring instruments (rule, Vernier callipers, micrometer, etc.) and recording the units correctly.

Mass

Mass refers to the amount of matter in an object, or how many atoms it contains, and is measured in grams or kilograms. The mass of an object is constant; it stays the same wherever the object is.

SI units and imperial units of length

Engineers all over the world need to be able to measure things accurately, but unfortunately there are two different systems of measurement in common use: SI units (metric) and imperial units (mainly used in the USA). Conversion from one system to the other can be done easily using readily available conversion tables.

Product life and reliability

Does a product last forever? No – it is important to appreciate that most products will eventually either become obsolete, due to developments in technology, or break down and become uneconomic to repair.

Consider a mobile phone. What is its lifespan? How reliable do you expect it to be? Do you expect it to work every day, providing you remember to charge the battery? If you buy a cheap mobile phone, do you expect it to be as reliable as an expensive phone, or do you simply expect the expensive phone to have more functions?

These are all things to consider in relation to a product's lifespan and reliability.

Performance, function and service requirements

Performance is how well a device, person or machine completes a task or activity. For example, a mobile phone's performance can be related to how well it picks up a signal from the mobile phone provider, so that texts and calls arrive promptly.

Service requirements describe the purpose for which a device or machine has been designed. For example, one of the functions of a mobile phone is to allow the user to receive texts.

A mobile phone must perform its basic function – that is, to allow people to make a phone call. How many other functions do people expect it to perform?

Economic and making considerations

Many products must be available at an economic price, that is, the highest amount of money that a person is willing to pay for the product or service.

Take mobile phones, for example. The market is very split by price, from top-end expensive phones to cheap phones. For a company manufacturing mobile phones to make a profit and stay in business, it needs to consider the following:

- developmental costs – research and development
- manufacturing costs – machines, raw product, package storage
- **logistics** – transport, shipping
- overheads – administration, rent, taxes, electricity and gas, and, of course, staff salaries and wages
- marketing and advertising.

Implications of standards and legislation

A manufacturer must abide by a country's standards and legislation. Standards vary by country, so what is acceptable in China may not be acceptable in England, for example. Therefore, companies have to adapt their products to accommodate these variations.

Imagine buying a laptop computer in the UK. The plug on the charger will fit electrical sockets in the UK, but you would not be able to use it in the United States, continental Europe or many other countries because they have different standards for electrical sockets.

For an engineering company, this variation in standards can be a very big hurdle to overcome, especially as UK companies also have to comply with British Standards.

Engineering drawing is a classic case of standardisation. Without standards, nobody would understand all of the abbreviations and projections.

DID YOU KNOW?

Engineers in the UK use multiple measurement systems. There is still occasional use of the imperial system, which includes feet and inches (distance), stones and pounds (weight), and gallons and pints (volume of liquids). Most UK companies use the metric (SI) system, which includes metres and millimetres, kilograms and grams, and litres.

Some items from other countries will use imperial measurements (particularly from the USA).

ACTIVITY

Find a conversion table for SI and imperial units.

KEY TERM

Logistics refers to the organisation and implementation of an operation, usually involving a lot of detail.

CHECK MY LEARNING

Product design specifications are very important.

1 Explain the difference between function and performance.

2 List the different types of information that should be included in a PDS.

Safe working

Legislation, particularly safety regulations, is critical to ensure safe working practices.

Legislation

Legislation is simply a collective term for all laws.

In the UK, an organisation called the Health and Safety Executive (HSE) is responsible for regulating workplace safety. Engineering workshops and premises without rules and regulations would be very dangerous places. Completion of a risk assessment is fundamental to your safety, and it is the law that for any hazardous operation a risk assessment needs to be carried out.

Risk assessment

A risk assessment involves looking carefully at a job or process to make sure it is being carried out safely.

The HSE recommends that a risk assessment is completed in five steps.

1 Identifying hazards

A hazard describes anything that might cause an accident or injury. Hazards can best be identified by inspecting your working environment and the equipment available to you. In an engineering environment, hazards might include:

- tools lying on the floor in an untidy workshop
- no guards on a drill
- warning signs not in place.

2 Deciding who might be harmed and how

The next stage is to think about who might be harmed, how that might happen, and the types of injury that might be caused.

3 Evaluating risk and adopting control measures

Risk measures the likelihood of a hazard causing an injury and how serious that injury is likely to be. A good way to begin measuring risk is to complete the standard HSE risk assessment pro forma, which is available online.

DID YOU KNOW?

One of the largest fines for a breach of HSE regulations was £1,125,000 for an oil company releasing gas in the North Sea.

Remember that you have a duty of care to yourself and others. If you fail that duty of care, you can be fined. The oil company failed a duty of care to others by putting them in danger.

---

4 Record your significant findings

Records of the risk assessment process and any actions taken to reduce risk should be recorded. Table 2.7 outlines this process.

◻ Table 2.7: Example of a risk assessment

What are the hazards?	Who might be harmed and how?	What is being done already?	What further action is necessary?	Action by whom?	Action by when?	Date
Tools on the floor in an untidy workshop	Staff or visitors to the workshop might trip over or slip on the tools on the floor, causing serious injury	Daily housekeeping at the end of the shift	Better housekeeping – ensure tools and equipment are cleared away immediately after use and not left until the end of the day	Production supervisor	Now	01/09/17
			Improve tool and equipment storage in the work area	Site maintenance manager	14/09/17	01/09/17

5 Review your assessment and update if necessary

Risk assessments should be reviewed regularly to ensure that they are still relevant and effective.

ACTIVITY

Research companies that have failed the duty of care. What were the consequences?

ACTIVITY

You are to disassemble a small, engineered product (for example, a motor or a pump). Follow these steps to carry out a risk assessment for this task.

1 Identify the hazards that may be present.

2 Decide who might be harmed and how.

3 Evaluate the risks and adopt control measures.

4 Record your findings.

5 Review your assessment and update if necessary.

6 Complete an HSE risk assessment pro forma for this task.

CHECK MY LEARNING

You have now learned what a risk assessment does and how it should be presented.

Explain the five stages of a risk assessment.

Learning aim B: assessment practice

How you will be assessed

In Component 2 you will be assessed by completing a series of internally set assignments.

When completing the assignment covering Learning Aim B, you will need to show that you can carry out a product investigation of an engineered product using disassembly techniques.

This will include demonstrating the ability to:

- disassemble (and then reassemble) an engineered product safely
- observe, measure and record engineering information
- write a detailed product design specification (PDS) based on a product investigation.

CHECKPOINT

Strengthen

- Describe the safe use of tools and equipment commonly used in the disassembly of engineered products.
- Name three pieces of equipment that could be used to measure linear dimensions.
- Name six types of mechanical fixings, classify them as semi-permanent or non-reusable and describe how they can be removed.

Challenge

- Name and then explain the importance of each element of a Product Design Specification (PDS).
- Which has the higher density: aluminium or steel? Which material would be the better choice for making handles for kitchen cupboard doors?

TIPS

Be systematic and methodical when disassembling an engineered product. Use photographs to record the position of components prior to their removal. Label the larger parts and store small parts in labelled ziplock bags. The notes, sketches and information you record during disassembly should be good enough to allow someone else to reassemble the product.

Description

In this assignment, you will be asked to investigate an engineered product by disassembling it, analysing how it works, how it was made and finally to write a Product Design Specification (PDS) to describe it.

Example tasks

Select a product that you are familiar with and is available for study and disassembly. Suitable products are similar to those considered in the assessment of Learning Aim A. These might be a: skateboard, roller skate, bicycle brake assembly, industrial light fitting, radio controlled car suspension assembly, or a cyclist's folding multi-tool.

You will then investigate the product's purpose and function.

- Carefully and safely dismantle the product; please ask your tutor for advice on the use of appropriate hand tools to do this.
- Lay out the parts and label them, identifying the name, materials used and the function of each one, in doing so you should examine visual features, surface features, mass, colour, degradation, and identification marks.
- Take some photographs of the labelled laid out parts that you can print and have available for the Shop Manager.
- For parts that have been machined/formed, measure their dimensions and record them on an inspection/dimensional data sheet and make a note of any component values.

Having carried out your dismantling activity:

- describe each component, their purpose and how they link together
- produce a product design specification [PDS] for the product that includes your reasons or evidence to support the specification. Make sure you have sections in your PDS that cover size and mass; product life and reliability; performance; function; service requirements; economic and making considerations; and the implications of standards and legislation.

Evidence

Your small folder should contain:

- annotated photographs of your labelled components
- inspection/dimensional data sheets
- written commentary showing a description of each component, their purpose and how they link together
- a competed product design specification (PDS).

TAKE IT FURTHER

Reflect on the disassembly process you carried out in the practice assessment. Write a detailed plan describing how you would organise this process in future, including any improvements. This might include some or all of the following:
- a list of all the personal protective equipment (PPE) used
- a list of safety precautions to be followed
- a list of all the tools required (including type and size)
- a list of documents you would need.

TIPS

Create a standard PDS document, with all the subheadings on it, before you start. This will prompt you to consider all the different elements that need to be covered.

Engineering make process 1

Planning the safe manufacture of any given engineered product is vital when honing your engineering skills – in both designing and making. When starting this process, the first thing you will need to think about is how to **define the problem.**

For example, imagine you are working with a designer to create a child's bicycle. List the potential problems you may have to overcome when designing this product.

You are now going to begin the process of preparing to make an engineered product. This needs careful planning and an understanding of the practical procedures.

The engineering design and make process can be very complex and detailed. You will produce solutions to problems using different combinations of practical engineering skills, including making, as part of the engineering process.

Define the problem

Brainstorming and carrying out market research, such as speaking to users of similar products or looking on the internet, can help narrow down the area you would like to focus on.

Once you have a problem you would like to explore, the next step is to identify the wants and needs of the end user. This could be done through observations and research.

Example

You have been asked to design a small wind turbine that can be used to charge a mobile phone while on camping trips. First, think about the needs of the user.

From research, it has been identified that the device must:

- charge a mobile phone from wind power alone
- affix easily to the top of a tent
- be convenient to transport
- be able to generate power in moderate wind conditions
- be totally waterproof
- be reliable and cost-effective.

You must now investigate similar products on the market to help establish suitable manufacturing techniques and to identify the engineering skills needed for production. To do this, you will need to analyse a similar existing product through disassembly.

As mentioned on page 110, product disassembly is important for many reasons. When you disassemble a product, you can learn a lot about the components, materials and fixings used within it. In terms of defining a problem, it is useful to ask yourself the following questions.

- What components would you need for the solution to your problem?
- What constraints would the size of these components impose?
- What other options/limitations will you have (for example, choices of switches or fastenings)?

Disassembling a product can help answer these questions, if you are looking to create a product similar to one that already exists.

Remember: you have to plan and make an engineered product, ensuring that it is made safely, to the correct sizes and within specified tolerances.

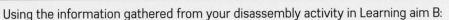

ACTIVITY

Using the information gathered from your disassembly activity in Learning aim B:

1 prepare a plan for the safe making of a reproduction of a component from the product you previously dismantled

2 prepare a list of the tools and materials needed to make the component

3 conduct a risk assessment of the processes to be used

4 make the component

5 inspect the quality of the component you made.

When choosing the component that you will make a reproduction of, it is important that you:

- check that you have the processes in the workshop to make this engineered component
- check that you have the materials available
- check that you have the measuring tools available
- ensure that you have the skills to make the engineered product.

Develop possible solutions

Once the problem has been clearly identified, and the needs/wants of the user fully understood, we can begin to develop some possible solutions that may solve the problem we are dealing with. Figure 2.10 is an example of some initial student solution ideas for a wood-burning stove:

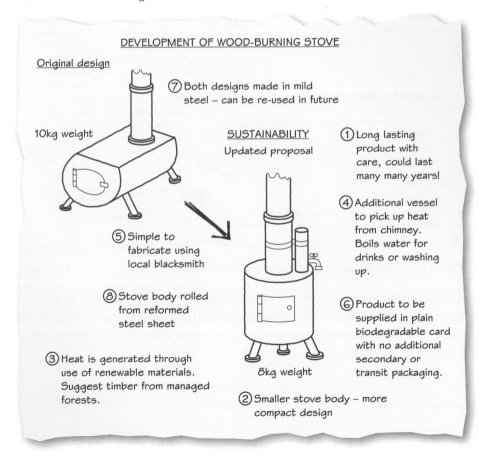

◼ Figure 2.10: Development of a wood-burning stove

Choose a solution

Figure 2.11 is an example of one student's chosen solution for the wind turbine charger for camping.

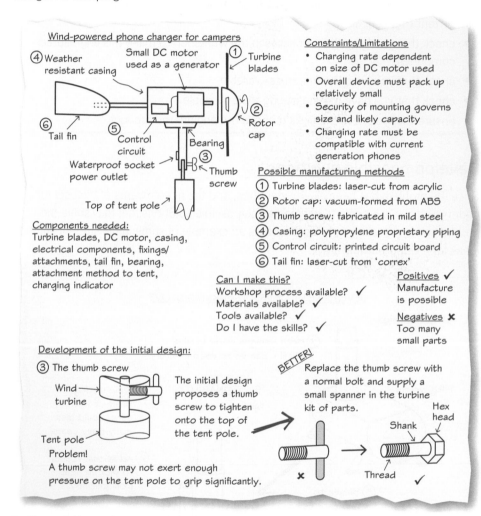

Figure 2.11: **Wind-powered phone charger for camping**

You can use this example to help you with the step of choosing a solution to an engineering problem. After careful consideration and analysis, the designer has made the decision to manufacture a bolt instead of the thumb screw. The bolt is similar to the one shown on page 106.

Once this decision has been made, an investigation into bolt sizes should be undertaken. Suppose that by careful measuring you found the bolt head to be 12 mm across flats, 15 mm across corners and 6 mm thick. It has an 8 mm thread with a thread length of 22 mm, and from the underside of the head to the end, the length of the bolt is 30 mm. You should use this information to draw or sketch the bolt (see Figure 2.12) to help you plan the making process.

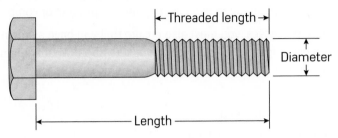

□ **Figure 2.12: Bolt dimensions**

Remember: there are always different ways to make a product. For example, a hole can be drilled on a drilling machine, a milling machine or by hand using a hand drill.

ACTIVITY

Examine the products you looked at in Learning aim B.

Prepare a document and see how many of the following points can be ticked off for each product.

1 Check that you have the processes in the workshop to make the engineered product.

2 Check that you have the materials available.

3 Check that you have the measuring tools available.

4 Ensure that you have the skills to make the engineered product.

5 Have you identified the possible problems and solutions for making the product?

6 Can you justify your solutions?

CHECK MY LEARNING

You have learned about defining a problem, developing possible solutions and choosing a solution. Write down a statement to describe one of the components from an engineered product that you have examined, and what the component is used for in the product.

Engineering make process 2

GETTING STARTED

Discuss in a small group what you need to do to ensure that you are fully prepared to make an engineering product using engineering processes.

Share your thoughts with other groups to add to your answers.

Making using engineering processes

Once you have defined a problem and decided on a solution, you need to plan the making of your component part. The activity on page 123 lists the main issues you need to consider when planning to make an engineered product or component part.

For all engineering processes, you must also ensure that you have all the necessary personal protective equipment (PPE). If you are unsure about what equipment you will need, look back at page 112 in Learning aim B.

You must list all of:

- the tools you are going to need
- the equipment you are going to need
- the machines you are going to need.

You also need to ensure that everything you need is available in your workshop.

ACTIVITY

Go to the workshop and see what materials, tooling and equipment are available to support your assessment activities.

DID YOU KNOW?

You need to be familiar with all of the operations needed and practise them if necessary. You are not allowed any help with the assessed work, apart from safety checking.

DID YOU KNOW?

It is important that you are fully prepared before starting to make an engineered product. Drawings and planning and inspection sheets need to be available. Keep notes in your logbook, take pictures for evidence, and get a Pearson BTEC observation document from your teacher to record your performance.

Example

The example of a bolt, described on page 123, sets out the different steps of making a component using engineering processes. Making a bolt will require various processes to be used. Refer back to Learning aim A for a reminder of the various operations that can be performed.

Step 1

This first step is to check if there is any hexagonal bar stock of the correct size available in the metal stores.

If not, you will need to use a round bar stock and mill a hexagon on the bar using a dividing head. You may need help from your teacher to set this up. An example of a dividing head is shown below.

◩ Dividing head

Step 2

If you wish, you can apply **engineer's blue** and mark the important dimensions on your bar stock.

When the milling is complete, or the hexagonal bar stock is obtained, you need to use a centre lathe to turn the 10 mm diameter by 30 mm length. Place a 45 degree chamfer on the end of the 10 mm bar.

When turning a diameter, make it slightly smaller for a thread, by about 0.1 of a millimetre. A die will not cut a thread successfully on a bar that is the same size as the thread. Always turn a 45 degree chamfer for the start of the thread (see Figure 2.13).

Check the lengths and diameters as you machine the bolt, and also check during roughing and finishing. Remember: a machine will take material off, but if you make the bolt too small you cannot put the material back on.

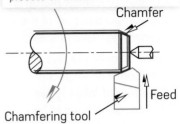

Chamfer

Feed

Chamfering tool

◾ Figure 2.13: Chamfering

ACTIVITY

Have you calculated the revolutions per minute (RPM) for the turning exercise on page 94? Now consider the feed rates you would need to use to turn the bolt, and work out the depth of cut for the roughing and finish turning operations.

Step 3

Set up an 8 mm die on a lathe and turn the chuck by hand anticlockwise while maintaining pressure on the tailstock, using it as shown in the picture below. Remember to stop at 22 mm so that you have 22 mm of thread.

◾ Using a die on a lathe

ACTIVITY

Following the steps in the example above, make a bolt to the specification detailed on page 123 in your workshop.

With a partner, evaluate each other's results. Did you do anything wrong? What could you do to improve your performance in making a component to a given specification?

CHECK MY LEARNING

The make process can be very different, depending on what component part you are making.

What size would you turn the diameter of the bar to take a 10 mm thread?

Engineering make process 3

GETTING STARTED

An inspection sheet record is a very important part of the engineering make process.

Research online to find a definition of an inspection sheet record. What types of information need to be recorded, and at what stage in the process should the inspection sheet record be filled in?

KEY TERM

Tolerances in engineering are the limits of variation allowed in the properties of a component.

Inspect and test chosen solution

An inspection sheet records in columns the required dimensions, the actual sizes, the **tolerances**, the pass or fail status of each inspection criterion, the inspection methods and the measuring instruments used for inspection.

An inspection sheet record is important because it helps the manufacturer ensure that the product fully complies with the original product specification.

As an example, think of the bolt from the previous two lessons. Consider the 8 mm diameter by 30 mm long bolt that is being turned. An entry in a record sheet might look something like Table 2.8.

 Table 2.8: Example data for a bolt in an inspection sheet record

Dimension	Actual size	Tolerance	Pass/Fail	Inspection method
8 mm diameter	7.9 mm	+0/−0.2 mm	Pass	Micrometer
30 mm length	29.5 mm	±0.1 mm	Fail	Vernier callipers
45 degrees	44.5 degrees	±0.25 degrees	Fail	Protractor

If we examine the 8 mm diameter requirement, the tolerance is +0/−0.2 mm. Therefore, the maximum size it could be is 8 mm and the minimum size it could be is 7.8 mm. As the diameter has been measured at 7.9 mm, it passes.

If we examine the 30 mm length requirement, the tolerance is ±0.1 mm. The maximum size it could be is 30.1 mm and the minimum size it could be is 29.9 mm. As the bolt is actually 29.5 mm long, it is too short, so it fails.

Also, because it is too short, the problem cannot be rectified, so it is scrap.

Process to complete the inspection sheet

The steps of completing an inspection sheet record like the one in Table 2.8 are as follows:

1 Complete the first column with the dimensions from the specification drawing.

2 Leave column 2 blank.

3 Fill in the tolerance from the specification drawing in column 3.

4 Leave column 4 blank.

5 Decide which measuring instrument to use to check each dimension and complete column 5.

6 Measure each dimension and record your results in column 2.

7 If a measurement is within tolerance, record a pass in column 4; if not, record a fail.

You must always sign the inspection sheet when you have finished, and date it.

Your teacher will give you an engineered product and an inspection sheet to fill in. Working in pairs, follow the guidance of your teacher to make the necessary measurements. Put the data into the inspection sheet using the step-by-step instructions and the example in Table 2.8 to help you.

Evaluate the outcome of a project

At the end of a project, you will be expected to present a detailed evaluation of the planning and making of the engineered product. If things have not turned out according to plan, make recommendations as to how to improve the manufacturing process in the future.

If your planning sequence is incorrect – for example, you stated that you would thread a hole prior to drilling it – record this observation in your logbook and state how you would remedy or overcome the problem if you were to make this product again. A simple reordering of the planning sheet would begin to solve this problem. Also, you would need to record if you corrected the planning sheet during the making of the bolt.

The 30 mm length dimension that is too short would need more evaluation to find out where the error arose. Was the length marked out incorrectly? Was it measured correctly during making? Were the stops on the machine set incorrectly?

Practise measuring some 10 mm bar stock with the following instruments:

1 Vernier callipers

2 micrometer

3 callipers and rule.

Record your findings and compare them with those of another student. Did your measurements agree? Were there any major discrepancies?

Create an inspection table, complete with all headings, that you could use to inspect an engineered component or product that you have made or will make.

List three things that you could report on when evaluating the outcome of your engineering project.

Developing a production plan

Planning is vital within engineering; if you don't plan correctly, you can easily make a mistake and your final product will be incorrect.

An engineering production plan includes the following features:

- health and safety in the workspace you will work in
- operations and processes you will use
- inspections, testing and quality standards
- a list of equipment and tools you will use
- a list of materials and components you will use
- the quantity of engineered product you will be making (for example, one-off, batch or mass production).

Developing a typical production plan

A production plan needs to show how a component or engineered product is made, and a person of a similar skill level as you should be able to understand and follow it. With a drawing and the plan, they should also be able to make the component or engineered product.

Table 2.9 shows a production plan prepared by a student. It is for the tail fin on the camper's wind turbine shown in Figure 2.11 on page 122.

◼ Table 2.9: Example of part of a production plan

Operations/ Processes	Tools and equipment	Materials	Health and safety	Inspection, testing and quality standards	Comments
Selecting material	• Tape measure • Micrometer	• 3 mm cast acrylic sheet	• Sharp edges • Heavy sheets	• Visual inspection	• Seek assistance with large sheets
Marking to suit sheet size for laser cutter	• Metre rule • Pencil • Engineer's square	• 3 mm cast acrylic sheet	• Sharp edges	• Re-check dimensions after marking	
Cutting to overall size	• Bandsaw	• 3 mm cast acrylic sheet	• Specific training to use bandsaw	• Check size after cutting • Check for surface scratches	• Seek assistance with large sheets
Laser cutting fin shape and edge finishing	• Laser cutter with extraction • Abrasive wet and dry paper	• Acrylic cut to overall size	• Sharp edges	• Dimension check • Touch test after smoothing edges	• Use water with abrasive paper

You will need to record on your production plan the results of inspections and testing and whether or not the item meets the quality standards for the component. These inspection results are often added to the comments column on completion.

ACTIVITY

With a partner, use the template shown in Table 2.10 to complete a production plan for the making of a bolt (see page 123 for the specification of the bolt). There should be enough detail about making processes and inspection procedures on pages 124–127 to get you started.

▣ Table 2.10: Layout of a production plan

Operations/ Processes	Tools and equipment	Materials	Health and safety	Inspection, testing and quality standards	Comments

CHECK MY LEARNING

Swap your production plan with that of another pair of students. Is there anything that you have missed? Update your plan with any information you missed, and also give feedback on the other pair's production plan.

Awareness of risks and hazards for making processes

Your health and safety is the most important thing there is. There are many hazards in an engineering workshop. For example, a milling machine cutter can remove a carelessly placed finger in milliseconds. So beware: an engineering workshop can be a very dangerous place.

Risks and hazards

A workshop can be full of risks and hazards, especially if it is not looked after properly. Before a practical task is begun, it is very important to prepare the area, readying it for work. During the task, all health and safety procedures should be followed, and activities must be undertaken with due care and attention. Upon completion of the task, the work area must be left clean, tidy and safe, in readiness to be used again.

- Moving parts – be alert to which parts are moving, and do not touch or approach these parts of a machine.

- Ensure machine guards are in place – guards are designed to protect you from getting trapped in a machine or being hit by parts coming off the machine or workpiece. You should know exactly which guards are required and how they work. Never try to reach over or around a machine guard.

- Use of the emergency stop – this is designed to quickly stop the machine. Before operating a machine, make sure you know the location of all emergency stops, and check that they work. Remember, the machine guard is often interlocked; this means that the machine will stop if the guard is moved during a machining operation.

- Machine isolation – this ensures that the machine is properly switched off (isolated) and cannot be accidentally activated. Make sure you know where all power switches and buttons are located, and check that they work.

- Wearing appropriate PPE – you should not enter a workshop unless you have the correct protective equipment. Overalls, safety boots and safety glasses are normally the minimum requirement, with other equipment, such as safety goggles or gloves, used for specific machining operations.

- Keeping a clean and tidy work area – all tools should be put away after use, **swarf** should be safely removed, and all spills should be quickly cleaned to prevent accidents. Never rest tools or workpieces on machines or machine tables – vibration can cause them to fall off, causing injury.

- Removing burrs and sharp edges – always use a tool to do this as they can be very sharp and can easily cut fingers.

- Identification of risks, associated hazards and their control – this is usually carried out using a risk assessment and should happen before any workshop activities begin. Has one been completed for your drilling, turning and milling operations?

 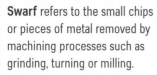

When you have finished in the workshop, clean your machine down and place any swarf in the appropriate bin, sweep up around your work area, and return the tools to the shadow boards or the stores.

Always leave a workshop as you would expect to find it.

ACTIVITY

Go to the Health and Safety Executive (HSE) website and study the sample risk assessment for a motor vehicle mechanical repair workshop.

Then complete a risk assessment for production of the bolt shown in Figure 2.12 on page 123.

ACTIVITY

Visit the engineering workshop in your centre and find the drilling machines, lathes and milling machines. Make a plan of the workshop to show the positions of the different machines, emergency stops, fire doors, first aid box etc., and annotate it with the following information.

1 Find and make a record of the guards that are on each machine.

2 Find out if each machine has an emergency stop.

3 Where are the emergency stops?

4 Find out how the tools are stored.

5 Find out what information is available about the cutting fluids.

6 Make a list of the PPE required for each machine.

CHECK MY LEARNING

Make sure that you are aware of any risks and hazards in your workshop. It is important to stay safe when you are working.

How do you isolate a machine in the workshop?

Where is the emergency stop on a lathe?

Safe preparation, good housekeeping and close down of the work area

GETTING STARTED

Being safe in a workshop does not just mean using tools and processes correctly. It is important to work in a safe way throughout: when preparing, working and finishing any engineering work.

Research basic lathe, milling and drilling processes. List the safe working practices that would be needed for each process. Think about every step of the process.

It is important that you use the correct tools and equipment in an engineering making process. If not, you will end up with poor surface finishes and incorrect dimensions.

Making skills associated with the product to be produced

It is important to practise the making skills you will need to make your component or engineered product. Your teacher can ensure that you are safe while you are practising, but then it is up to you to work safely and independently from your production plan.

DID YOU KNOW?

There are many videos online showing basic lathe and milling processes. But beware: they do not all show the machines being operated safely. They may not have guards on the chuck, and many operators may not be using the correct PPE. Ask your teacher to show you the correct process if you are unsure.

Appropriate set-up of the work area/machine

You need to prepare the work area where you will complete practical tasks. This could be either a workbench or the area around a machine. You will need to make sure that the area is safe. For example, there should be no obstructions that could become tripping hazards. You also need to check that all of the tools, equipment and materials you will need to use are available, and that these are safe to use.

Each machine in a workshop has its own specific requirements for safe operation. Your teacher will let you use a machine only if it is in good condition, it has been serviced and maintained correctly and you have the necessary skills and training to use it effectively and safely. The general workshop area should be set up appropriately according to the tasks being undertaken.

For example, if a process is likely to produce fumes (e.g. spray painting), then sufficient extraction and ventilation must be provided. If a job requires metal to be arc welded, a safe area with light shields and fume extraction must be set up before the welding commences.

Adaptation according to inspected outcomes

We all make mistakes, and sometimes you need to make changes or adaptations to a component because of mistakes you have made in the making process. When you check and inspect a component, you may find that it is not quite as it should be, and you will need to make a decision about whether to adapt what you have done, or to start again. You could adapt a design by giving it rounded corners if cutting has not been accurate, as long as the component will still perform the function it was designed for.

When a product has been completed in the workshop, it then needs to be inspected to see if it fully matches the original specification. This may involve quality checks, dimensional checks, strength testing and visual aesthetic checks. If the product fails any of the checks (does not meet the specification), it may need to be adapted or altered so that it is correct. A customer will not accept a product that is not what they asked for. A product that is not safe, or is not capable of correctly doing the job it was designed to do, is also unacceptable.

ACTIVITY

1   Prepare a list of everything that should be checked before anyone undertakes any practical activity in your school workshop.

2   Choose one machine in your workshop and list all of the checks that should be done before using that machine.

3   Prepare a poster to display on the workshop wall explaining the procedures that should be followed when closing down the workshop after practical activity has finished.

CHECK MY LEARNING

Working with a partner, discuss:

1   the procedures and safety precautions to be followed when setting up and using a centre lathe, a milling machine, an arc welder and a pillar drill

2   the checks a workshop technician should perform before anyone starts practical activity in a work area.

Choosing suitable tools

Once you have studied your plans and fully understood the requirements of the task to be undertaken, you will need to select the required materials from the storage area. It will then be time to actually start the making process.

However, there is often more than one way to produce a certain part of your product, and you will need to decide on which method you are actually going to use to make the part. When you have decided exactly how you are going to proceed, you will then need to select the appropriate tool to perform the task. This may require in-depth knowledge about the capabilities of each tool or machine–tool combination. You must ask for help from your supervisor or workshop technician if you are not one hundred per cent sure. Using the wrong tool could ruin your work, and it could also be extremely dangerous.

The lists below show the many different tools you might use on a lathe, drill or milling machine, as well as the functions they perform.

Tools for drilling

- Centre drill – the tool often used to machine the first indent in the workpiece that acts as an accurate guide for the following machining operation using a drill bit.
- Drill bit – the tool that is used to produce the drilled holes (sometimes called a twist drill). It often follows the use of a centre drill to ensure the tool is accurately aligned to the workpiece when being used.
- Flat-bottomed drill – a drill bit without a point that is used to produce blind holes (holes that do not go all the way through the material but need a flat bottom).
- Counterboring tool – a flat-bottomed drill with some of its flutes removed that is used to enlarge an existing hole, allowing a fastener to sit below the surface of the workpiece. Spotfacing is similar to counterboring, but a shallower version of a counterbore is used to ensure that a small flat area is created for a seal or washer to fit into.
- Countersinking tool – similar to a drill bit but smaller in length, it is used to produce an angled start to the hole that is used for a screw or bolt of similar shape and form to fit into.
- Reamer – a tool used after drilling to produce an accurate hole with a very smooth finish.
- Tap – another tool used after drilling to produce a thread in the hole.

Lathe tools

- Turning tool – removes material from the workpiece along its circumference.
- Facing tool – removes material from the end of a workpiece to produce a flat surface. The tool is moved at right angles to the workpiece.
- Form tool – produces a very specific shape or profile, such as a radius or stepped feature.
- Parting-off tool – produces deep grooves, which will cut off the workpiece at a specific length.
- Single-point threading – used when a thread form needs to be cut into the outside diameter of the workpiece.

- Boring bar – used on a lathe to carry out boring operations along the axis of a workpiece, such as increasing the size of a drilled hole.
- Recessing tool – often used after boring operations to produce internal features, such as a recessed groove.
- Centre drill, twist drill/drill bit, reamer and tap – these are the same as for drilling.
- Die – similar to a tap but cuts a thread on an external diameter.
- Knurling tool – produces a diamond pattern, known as a knurl, on the outside of the workpiece.

ACTIVITY

Working in pairs, use a lathe to cut a piece of 25 mm diameter bar, 100 mm long down to 23 mm diameter for a length of 25 mm. Think about any safety considerations before you begin – what tools will you need to complete this task?

Tools for milling

- Face mill – a cutter with multiple cutting tips, often called inserts, designed to move across the face of the workpiece.
- End mill – the most common tool used in milling; this has cutting teeth at one end and along the sides.
- Slot drill – a type of end mill designed to plunge into the workpiece like a drill bit and then be moved across to create a groove or enclosed slot.
- Slotting cutter – cutter with multiple tips designed to move through a workpiece to create a channel or slot.
- Slitting saw – disc with saw teeth around the perimeter, designed to cut deep, thin slits into the workpiece.
- Profile cutter – designed to produce a specific shape or profile, such as gears or corner radii.
- Twist drill/drill bit, reamer and boring tool/boring bar – these are the same as for drilling or turning.

ACTIVITY

You have been tasked with producing an aluminium bar that:

1 has a 45 degree chamfer on one end
2 has an overall radius of 10 mm
3 is parted off from the stock bar
4 is faced off on the end without the chamfer.

What are the correct tools to use?

ACTIVITY

You are to drill a hole of 10 mm diameter. Explain the sequence of steps you will take, using the correct tools.

CHECK MY LEARNING

You have learned about a range of tools that are used for drilling, turning and milling processes. With a partner, make a list of three tools that are used for each type of operation, and sketch the features produced by these tools.

Skills in observing and recording techniques

KEY TERM

Quality control is the set of procedures that are followed to ensure that the quality of a product is maintained and manufacturing errors are reduced or eliminated.

Examining an engineered product is a very important step in the engineering design and make process, because it forms the basis of **quality control**. The very best producers of engineered goods, such as the major car manufacturers, spend millions of pounds inspecting their products, both during production and upon completion. If substandard products find their way to customers, the resulting negative feedback could be very damaging to sales of the product and to the reputation of the manufacturer.

As an engineer, you need to be able to observe what is happening when you are carrying out an engineering activity. This does not simply mean watching the process – you also need to use your other senses.

You might notice that a process is very noisy, which could mean that the feed rate or speed of a machine needs to be changed. There may be some unusual smells, which could indicate that more coolant is needed, or a workpiece might be vibrating, which could mean it is working loose from the holding device. You need to be aware of such signs when observing an engineering operation.

You also need to observe the outcomes of an activity – for example, the accuracy of dimensions and surface finishes, as well as the ability of components to fit together as designed. We have already looked at how to record findings; often this will be in the form of an inspection report or as notes on the production plan.

The checking process involves taking accurate measurements from your manufactured parts or product and comparing your results with the measurements specified on your plans. There may be other important checks too, such as a simple visual check or an actual full operational test of the whole product. For example, an aircraft manufacturer will fly a new aeroplane and thoroughly check all of the systems and capabilities before it is handed over to the customer.

Measurements taken from a completed article are always checked against the original specification figures. These are called comparisons. Measurements taken during the activity of manufacture are called process measurements.

Process measurement

Process measurement is one way of checking how effective an engineering process is. It allows you to find and solve problems that occur during a manufacturing task. For example, if a drilling operation is not as accurate as it should be, you can use process measurement to find the causes.

You can also take measurements during an activity to make sure that the outcome is going to meet the specification – for example, using callipers to check the diameter of a workpiece that is being turned on a lathe. Taking regular measurements will help to prevent the workpiece from being made too small.

You should take measurements of your manufactured parts during the process of manufacture, in addition to checking them upon completion.

Comparisons

When you make comparisons between measurements, you will need to base these on the 'true measurement' – in other words, the measurements set out in the specification, along with the tolerances that are given. You should always take more than one measurement reading, just in case you make a mistake. If the second reading is different from the first, do the measurement again. You should always check the accuracy of the measuring equipment that you use – for example, by measuring something that has known dimensions.

In order to check that the manufactured parts and the product you have produced fully satisfy the original specification, you will have to take measurements and compare them with those originally given by the customer. You may also compare the measurements against an exemplar part that has been checked and approved to be within the required tolerances.

For example, if a bolt is specified as needing to be 60 mm long, with a tolerance of plus or minus 0.5 mm, it must be a minimum of 59.5 mm and a maximum of 60.5 mm in length. If your measurements show that your bolt is not within this allowable range, you will need to take action to correct the part.

If your manufactured component is not within tolerance, you should find out why this is the case and suggest ways in which the manufacturing process could be changed to ensure that future manufactured parts are accurate and within tolerance.

ACTIVITY

1 Using a micrometer and Vernier callipers, measure the length and thread diameter of a selection of bolts with the same specification (e.g. all M6 × 30 mm from the same supplier). Collect and record the data you obtain in a chart.

2 Identify from your data the maximum and minimum sizes you have measured and suggest what the manufacturer's tolerances are for the bolt length and thread diameter.

DID YOU KNOW?

Making errors with measurements can be very costly. For example, the aerospace engineering teams in Europe and the USA used different units of measurement when calculating the trajectory of the Mars Climate Orbiter spacecraft launched in 1998. The following year, the craft entered the Martian atmosphere at the wrong angle and disintegrated as a result!

For your engineering work, always use the metric (SI) system.

CHECK MY LEARNING

Make sure you understand why measurements need to be taken during and after an engineering process.

Why should measurements of each aspect of a component or product be taken more than once?

Why should you check the accuracy of measuring equipment?

Learning aim C: assessment practice

How you will be assessed

In Component 2 you will be assessed by completing a series of internally set assignments.

When completing the assignment covering Learning Aim C, you will need to show that you can create a detailed production plan and carry out the manufacture of an engineered component.

This will include demonstrating the ability to:

- plan the stages of the engineering make process, including the selection of the most appropriate manufacturing method(s) and appropriate inspection and testing
- carry out engineering processes
- evaluate the outcome of the make process
- develop a comprehensive production plan
- understand the risks associated with make processes, and work safely.

CHECKPOINT

Strengthen

- Why do you need to inspect components once you have made them?
- Why should you make notes on your production plan as you work through the different steps?
- Make a list of the risks associated with common workshop activities, and explain how these risks are controlled.

Challenge

- Carry out a comprehensive risk assessment on a range of common workshop activities including the use of machine tools.
- Why is it important to close down a work area on completion of practical tasks? What could happen if it is not closed down correctly?

ASSESSMENT ACTIVITY   LEARNING AIM   C

Description

In this assignment you will be asked to reproduce a component from the product disassembled during the assessment of Learning Aim B. This should be carried out using the same materials and similar making processes as the original manufacturer.

Example tasks

You must select an engineered component from the product you studied in the assignment for Learning Aim B (e.g. a turned polyurethane wheel if you studied a skateboard, a machined steel tool if you studied a folding bicycle multi-tool).

You should then create a production plan to enable you, or another competent person, to make the component safely. Make sure that your plan covers:

- health and safety
- operations/processes
- inspection, testing and quality standards
- equipment/tools

TIP

Your production documentation (including planning sheets, notes, drawings, sketches and calculations) are working documents. If you encounter any problems then add corrections and explanatory notes to them as you work.

- materials and components
- quantity
- how the selected engineered products will be inspected and checked.

Having developed your plan you need to make the component.

- Make some notes on a copy of your plan that shows any anticipated problems and your suggested solutions, and identifies important safety considerations.
- Discuss what you have done with your tutor before starting to make the component.
- Obtain the correct materials.
- Set up the work area/machine before you start making the component.
- Obtain the permission of your tutor before you commence making your component.
- Make your component.
- Obtain some photographs of you making your component – print and annotate these to show what you are doing.

Having made your component you need to provide information about its accuracy.

- Inspect your component and record the measurements and other quality observations.
- Close down and tidy up your work area.
- Finally you need to reflect on your plan and the manufacturing processes you used and write about the plan and processes success and about any improvements you can suggest.

Evidence

Evidence could include:

- your original production plan
- copy of your production plan showing your notes
- annotated photographs of you making your component
- inspection/dimensional – record of the measurements and other observations on quality
- written commentary showing your evaluation of the success of your production plan and any improvements.

Your finished component should also be available.

TIPS

Work safely, and do not take any risks. Be careful when following guidance in YouTube videos: there is a lot of unsafe practice shown in some clips. Your teacher will be able to tell you which videos show the correct guidance.

TAKE IT FURTHER

When you have completed the making of your component, you need to look at it in detail to see how well it compares to the original.

Write down the good points and the bad points of both your plan and your practical making activities. What went well and what could be improved? Use these comments to suggest ways in which planning and making activities might be done differently when you complete another similar activity to improve the outcome.

COMPONENT

3

Responding to an Engineering Brief

Introduction

As an engineer, you need to be able to investigate and find solutions to problems in a given engineering brief. In this component, you will build on the skills and knowledge you have learned in Components 1 and 2 and apply these to solve problems. This will include testing, collecting and analysing data, evaluating results and issues, and suggesting possible solutions.

In this component, you will explore methods that can be used to respond to an engineering brief. To help guide you through the process, you will look at ways of meeting the needs of the engineering brief, methods of generating a design solution and, finally, means of selecting and presenting a solution.

You will develop a range of skills that will help you to find a solution to a problem and to produce and present varied ideas, including techniques used to share these ideas.

LEARNING AIMS

In this component you will:

A	carry out a process to meet the needs of an engineering brief
B	provide a design solution for an engineered product against the needs of an engineering brief
C	provide solutions to meet the needs of an engineering brief.

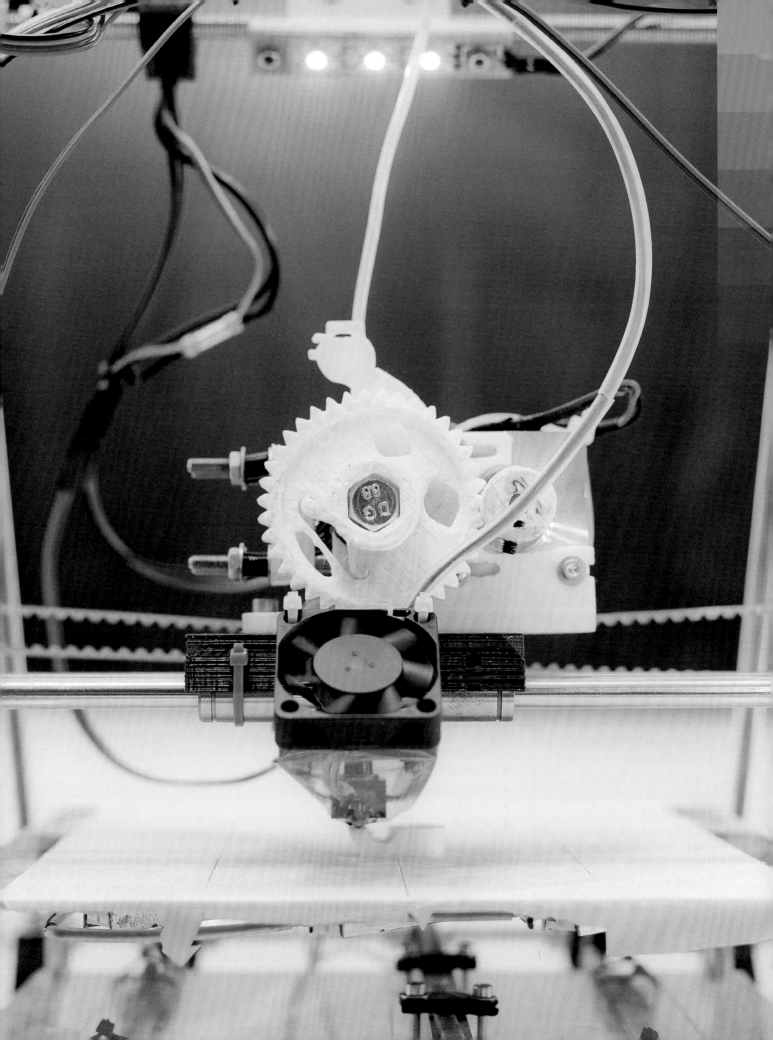

Carry out a process

Working in pairs, discuss how useful you think instructions are within engineering processes and why they are used.

Engineering processes

◼ **Example of a model construction kit**

When you are carrying out engineering processes, it is important that you have clear instructions to follow.

These work instructions can be provided in lots of different ways, but the reasons for using them are usually the same:

- making sure processes are carried out in the correct way
- reducing the likelihood of mistakes because each step is listed
- ensuring the correct tools are used because they are named in the work instructions.

Work instructions

Some examples of work instructions that can be used for engineering activities include:

- flow charts that show individual stages
- schematic drawings and diagrams
- process documentation
- job cards
- production plans.

Have you ever assembled a model construction kit or helped or watched someone assemble some flat-pack furniture, using the instructions and any hand tools provided? Think about any difficulties or issues that arose. What would it have been like without the instructions?

Working with the same partner as for the Getting Started activity above, think about and make a list of the advantages and disadvantages of having work instructions. Compare your ideas with the class group.

In Component 2: Learning aim C, you developed a production plan for the manufacture of a component for an engineering product. Think about the information you included and your reasons for including it.

One way of providing work instructions for an activity is to use a flow chart that sets out the stages of the process. Alternatively, graphical instructions can be effective, such as the sequential drawing shown in Figure 3.1.

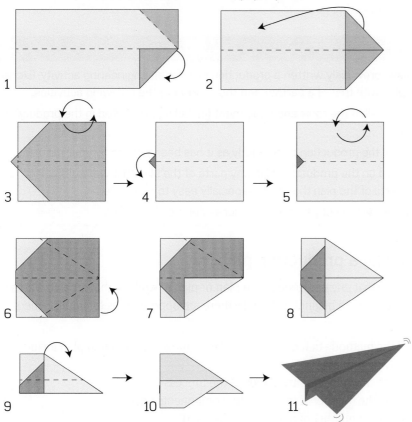

Instructions: How to make a paper plane

□ Figure 3.1: A sequential drawing for making a paper plane

Following planned procedures

Working in a small group, discuss what could happen if you did not follow the instructions correctly when replacing a part on a bicycle or a skateboard.

Sometimes it is easy to make a mistake when you are carrying out a sequence of activities, even if there are only a small number of parts that need to be assembled to complete the product.

ACTIVITY

You have previously written a production plan for an engineering activity. Exchange your plan with that of a partner and then carry out the following activities.

1 Collect all of the tools and equipment (including PPE) listed in the production plan.

2 Follow the production plan exactly as it has been written by your partner.

3 Record on the production plan any parts of the plan that were difficult to follow, or parts of the plan that were especially easy to complete.

4 Discuss with your partner how successful the plans were.

Improving a production plan

It is unlikely that any new production plan or plan of working that anyone writes will be perfect from the beginning. Usually there are opportunities for improvements to be made.

Some of the methods that could be used to improve a production plan include:
- simplifying the task
- removing any unnecessary stages of the process
- reducing the number of tools and/or components needed
- reducing the number of machines to be used.

ACTIVITY

Take the production plan for an engineering activity that you previously used and try to improve it using the suggested ideas above.

1 Highlight any stages in the plan where the tasks could be simplified.

2 Note any stages that could be removed or combined.

3 Are there opportunities to reduce the number of components, tools or pieces of equipment used?

- ◼ **If possible, try to reduce the number of different tools and items of equipment when improving a production plan**

One other way to improve the efficiency of production is to use standardised components wherever possible, such as using the same diameter of fixings so that the same tool can be used to tighten them – for example, using M6 machine screws with a cross head for all fixings. This reduces the number of tools needed to fit the fixings, and also standardises the drill bits needed to produce holes in the components.

CHECK MY LEARNING

You have learned how to follow a production plan to carry out an engineering process. You have also looked at ways of improving production plans, for example, by making processes more efficient.

With a partner, compare your original and improved production plans and discuss why the improved plans are better.

Prototypes and models

KEY TERM

Prototypes are a first version of a product from which other forms are developed.

Prototypes and models are an important part of the development of most products, not just those in engineering. Some products are only ever produced in prototype or model form, as only one is needed.

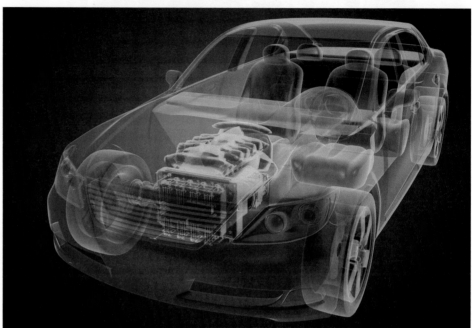

■ Not all prototypes are physical – many modern engineered products are prototyped virtually using very powerful computer simulation software

DID YOU KNOW?

Formula One racing teams use very powerful prototyping software that simulates how a car will perform on different motor racing tracks. This allows them to use actual track time more effectively.

Why prototype?

The main reason for prototyping is to prevent expensive mistakes from happening. It is much better to produce one example of a product and then test it extensively than to make thousands of examples for sale, only for them to fail after a short period of use.

The use of prototypes and models allows an engineer to find any faults or problems with a design before it is made on a large scale. It is normal for lots of prototypes to be made as part of the development process, as improvements can often be found in a design.

Prototypes are made for many products that are developed by engineers. Find an example of a prototype of a product that you are interested in and make notes on the following.

1 Research the tests that were performed on the prototype.

2 Find out how many different prototypes were made.

3 Compare the final design with the original prototype – how similar are the two?

Testing of prototypes

It is better to make a mistake with the design and manufacture of a prototype than with the final product. This is why testing of prototype designs is an important stage of the design process. For this, you could include the use of functional, ergonomic and/or destructive tests.

You might also use your prototypes to experiment with a design, maybe by reducing material use or by changing the processes used to make the components.

Functional tests

Functional tests are carried out to see if the design works correctly. This might include checking that any moving parts move as they should or that the prototype will fit onto an item that it is designed for – for example, checking that a new design of protective case will fit onto the tablet computer or mobile phone for which it was intended.

Ergonomic tests

Ergonomic tests are carried out to check that the design is easy to use. If a product is to be used by people, it must be easy to use. Controls must be accessible, and it should be obvious what needs to be done to make it work. Colour might also be an important factor to consider, with contrasting colours used to make things stand out.

Destructive tests

Destructive tests are carried out to see how difficult it is to break the product. Sometimes you will need to know how much force can be applied to the product before parts break off or snap. This can be very important if the product is going to be exposed to strong forces and high loads when it is being used.

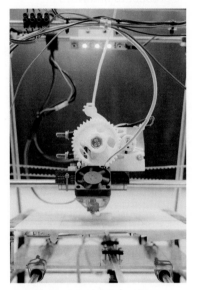

■ **3D printing can be used for producing prototypes both in industry and in school**

It is important to make prototypes or models, or use virtual prototypes, to check that a design will work as intended.

With a partner, discuss what might happen if prototypes of certain engineered products were not tested, for example, a car engine or a digital camera.

Understanding how a product is assembled

GETTING STARTED

Have you heard of the term reverse engineering? With a partner, discuss the reasons why design engineers may need to disassemble a product to find ways of improving it.

One method of developing a product is to look in detail at what is already available. This can be done in a number of ways, although one of the most effective methods is known as reverse engineering.

Reverse engineering

Reverse engineering is the process of disassembly and analysis of a product to investigate how it was manufactured and the purpose of the components from which it is made.

Reverse engineering can include some, or all, of the following:
- disassembling the product down to its component parts
- analysing the design features of the product and its components.

◘ **When reverse engineering a product, remember to do this logically and record all stages of the process**

Disassembly

Disassembling a product is the first stage of a reverse engineering exercise. It is good practice to lay out all the component parts of the product so that they can be analysed in turn. Do the following:
- If possible, locate any assembly drawings for the product you are disassembling.
- Make sketches, or take photographs, of every stage of the process.
- Note down details of each component, especially any numbers, values or marks that they may have.
- List the tools and equipment used at each stage of the process. Your records should be good enough to allow another person to be able to put the product back together again.

Practise disassembly on a product that has at least six components (perhaps an old unimportant product that is no longer required).

1 Disassemble the product, making notes of all the tools and equipment used at each stage.

2 Produce sketches to show the order of disassembly.

3 Use your sketches and notes to produce a plan for the reassembly of the product.

Disassembling a product can be a vital stage in the development of something new. While you are not going to copy the design, it will give you an idea of how the original product was made, what the components are and what they are used for, and the stages of manufacture.

You can use a product disassembly exercise to help plan production and redesign components or a whole product. Whenever possible, you should make sketches of the parts of the product and the stages you have completed. These could be used to produce exploded diagrams and assembly drawings, which will be covered later.

Make a list of all the components and the order in which you have removed them from the product. It could be a problem if you have taken a motor apart and then find, when you think you have finished putting it all back together again, that there are three screws and a spring left over!

LINK IT UP

Later in Component 3, different methods of presenting engineering information, including exploded diagrams, will be investigated.

DID YOU KNOW?

Reverse engineering is not just used to analyse an existing product to see how it works. Many classic cars, steam railway engines and old aircraft are still in use today only because of reverse engineering. It has allowed engineers to manufacture replacements for obsolete components.

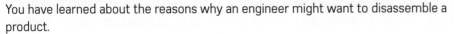
■ Disassembling a product can also help if you need to repair the product later

CHECK MY LEARNING

You have learned about the reasons why an engineer might want to disassemble a product.

Working in pairs, think about the different tools you will need to use when disassembling an engineered product.

Handling and using materials, equipment and machinery

GETTING STARTED

Make a list of the types of metals that you think can be used in an engineered product.

Materials can be categorised in different ways. In engineering, we often think about metals, polymers, composites and smart materials.

Using materials

> **LINK IT UP**
>
> In Component 2: Learning aim A, you looked at various materials that are used to make engineered products.

KEY TERM

Alloys are mixtures of two or more metals that have improved properties and characteristics..

Ferrous metals

These are metals that contain iron. Other metals are often added to iron to produce ferrous **alloys**. Materials such as stainless steel and high carbon steel are examples of ferrous metals.

Non-ferrous metals

These are metals that do not contain any iron. They can be pure metals, such as copper or titanium, or they can be alloys, such as brass and bronze. Sometimes non-ferrous metals are alloyed with ferrous metals, as is the case with stainless steel. Normally, the alloying process improves the properties of a material – for example, to make it stronger or more resistant to corrosion.

Thermosetting polymers

These are polymers that can be heated and formed once, but after that they cannot be re-formed. They are useful for applications where a lot of heat is produced, such as in electrical fittings or domestic appliances, e.g. kettles.

Thermoforming polymers

Unlike thermosetting polymers, thermoforming polymers can be heated time and time again and re-formed each time. Some of the common thermoforming materials you may have come across include acrylic and polystyrene.

Safe handling of materials

For each type of material, there are specific handling methods that need to be followed carefully. For example, when handling sheet steel, you will need to wear protective gloves because of the sharp edges, safety boots because of the weight (in case you drop the material), and work overalls to protect your skin and prevent clothing from becoming dirty.

If materials are hot, you will need to wear heat-proof safety gloves. Safety glasses should be worn to protect your eyes whenever you are cutting materials or handling awkward or long lengths of material that could catch you in the eye.

The form and shape of the material supplied can impact on safe handling procedures. Most metals are purchased in a specific form. However, polymers can be supplied as a resin or a powder. This can lead to a whole different set of safety hazards and safe working requirements.

Many material forms are supplied with a safety data sheet, which will give information on:

- safe handling and storage requirements
- PPE that should be worn
- what to do if there is an accident or spillage.

You should always try to transport and use materials in their safest form. For example, if you are able to cut a 3 m length of bar material into smaller sections before moving it from stores to where it is needed, then you should try to do this.

Using equipment and machinery

You should only use equipment and machinery that you have been instructed how to operate, so you are aware of the safe working practices that need to be followed.

Some equipment and machines can only be used with certain materials. It is therefore important to check that the equipment or machinery is suitable for the process. Always get permission before using any piece of equipment or machinery.

CHECK MY LEARNING

You have revisited the types of material that can be used to make an engineered product. You have also looked at forms of supply for materials.

In a small group, discuss why specific equipment is used with certain materials.

ACTIVITY

Engineers work with many different types of material, each with different handling requirements.

1 Research methods of handling a range of metallic and polymer materials.
2 List the safe working practices advised for each material.
3 Record the PPE that should be used and the reasons for its use.

◻ Materials are available in many forms and shapes

Recording the process

KEY TERMS

Accuracy depends on the way in which measurements are taken and how they are recorded.

Degree of accuracy is half a unit on either side of the unit of measure; if the unit is 1, then any measurement between $9\frac{1}{2}$ and $10\frac{1}{2}$ will be measured as 10.

Reliability depends on there being only small variations in data and measurements being within tolerance.

Precision refers to the closeness of two or more measurements to each other. For example, if you weigh a given substance five times, and get 3.2 kg each time, then your measurement is very precise.

Measuring and recording data

For the results of investigations to be useful, data must be recorded correctly. This means that information must be recorded with accuracy and precision, categories need to be decided, and you should use the correct units for measurements.

Accuracy

When you record data, it is important to record values with **accuracy**. This means that any measurements are within an agreed tolerance level. For example, the measurements of the length of a machine screw could be recorded in millimetres instead of taking measurements to a fraction of a millimetre. This is also known as **degree of accuracy**. It is important that you also record values against the correct data group, otherwise the results will be unreliable.

Reliability is important when analysing information. If there are mistakes in measurements or recorded data, the results will not be reliable and could lead you to draw the wrong conclusion and thereafter make decisions that are not appropriate. When you collect and record data, you need to make sure that your data are both accurate and reliable.

Precision

When you are recording data, one of the decisions that you will need to make is the degree of **precision** required. This will depend on what you want to use the data for. If it is to find out the average time it takes to complete a task, then the level of precision will be quite high; if you need to find out how many pan head machine screws you have, then the level of precision will be low – unless you want to know how many of each different length you have.

When you decide on the level of precision needed for your data collection, you should think about the following questions:

- Can the data be divided in more than one way?
- How important is it to divide the data into very small groups?

Units of measurement

When you record data from investigations, you need to choose units of measurement that are sensible and appropriate. For example, if you were timing how long it takes a ball to roll down a ramp, a sensible unit of measurement would be seconds, not minutes or hours. The lengths of fixings would be sensibly measured in millimetres, not metres or kilometres. However, the distance a car travels in an hour would be better measured in kilometres.

LINK IT UP

Component 2: Learning aim B covered practical skills for measuring diameters and linear dimensions and methods to find out the values of electronic components.

Tabulation of data

When you collect data, you will also need to record it. This is probably best done using a table where you can include the categories the data are split into and the units of measurement. It is probably easiest to use a tally chart, as shown in Table 3.1, to record sets of data where large quantities are involved.

You could also record exact values in a data collection chart like the one shown in Table 3.2, which has been used to record data on the load applied to and the resultant extension of a metal component.

▫ **Table 3.1: Tally chart**

Diameter of screw (mm)	Tally	Total
4	⠀卌 卌 卌 III	18
5	卌 卌 II	12
6	卌 卌 卌 卌 III	23
8	卌 卌 卌 IIII	19

▫ **Table 3.2: Data collection chart**

Load–Extension data								
Load (newtons)	50	75	100	125	150	175	200	225
Extension (mm)	14	26	38	50	62	74	86	98

ACTIVITY

Working with a partner, collect a random selection of either mechanical fixings or electronic components. Separate the components into groups or categories and carry out investigations into the following (record the results with accuracy so that they are reliable):

1 Take measurements using suitable measuring equipment, or read the values of the components.

2 Record the results of the investigation in a table.

Once complete, discuss what you think the information from the results shows.

CHECK MY LEARNING

You have learned about different methods of presenting data, including the use of tabulation.

Using a set of data related to either mechanical or electronic components, tabulate the data by categorising the components and recording the numbers of each. With a partner, discuss how accurate your results are, how good your chosen categories are, and whether and how you could improve the accuracy of the results if you were to undertake the same activity again.

Displaying data using charts and graphs

KEY TERMS

Trends are patterns in data, e.g. values might increase for one variable as the values decrease for another.

Charts are usually used when data are being presented in groups.

Graphs are used to plot individual data values.

We have looked at ways in which data can be recorded from investigations. Next we discuss how the data may be displayed. This can be done graphically using **charts** and **graphs**.

When deciding which type of graph or chart to use, you need to think about the type of data you are showing and what information about the data you want to share. For example, the results of an investigation into the diameter of screws could be presented in a graphical chart, where shapes are used to represent data. Alternatively, a graph could be plotted for the load–extension investigation in Table 3.2, with a line graph used to represent the data.

There are many types of chart and graph that are used to present data. Some are listed in Table 3.3.

▣ **Table 3.3: Types of chart and graph**

Chart type	Graph type
Pie chart	Line graph
Bar chart	Scatter graph
Pictograph	

Types of chart

To compare the types of chart, look at how the data collected for the diameter of screws in Table 3.1 can be presented in different ways:

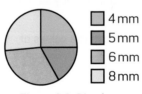

▣ Figure 3.2: Pie chart

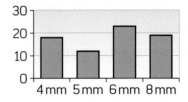

▣ Figure 3.3: Bar chart

Screw size	
4 mm	
5 mm	
6 mm	
8 mm	

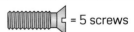
= 5 screws

▣ Figure 3.4: Pictograph

Pie charts are good for showing the relationship between individual groups of data and the total amount of data. They show each group as a proportion of the total. In Figure 3.2, each sector, or slice of the pie, represents the quantity of each size of screw as a proportion of the total number of screws.

Bar charts are useful for identifying trends, such as what is most popular or what happens the most. In Figure 3.3, it is easy to see that there are more 6 mm screws than the other sizes. The **scale** of the chart is important, so check the scale on the y-**axis** and try to use scales that are easy to interpret. Vertical bar charts are also known as column charts.

Pictographs show data by using images. In Figure 3.4, each picture of a screw represents five actual screws, which can be confusing when the data is not in groups of five. Pictographs can be useful if you are presenting data about numbers of items or activities completed, but it is important to choose a sensible value for each image to represent. If each screw represented one actual screw in Figure 3.4, then you would need to draw 23 screws for the 6 mm screw size, which would be time-consuming. Alternatively, if each image of a screw represented 100 actual screws, the values would be hard to work out because the images of partial screws would be small and very similar to each other.

KEY TERMS

Axis is the name of either the horizontal or the vertical line that is used to show the scale of the graph or chart.

A **scale** on a graph is used to show the quantity of each group.

ACTIVITY

Using data you have collected or that your teacher has provided, produce an example of each different type of chart. It is important that you present the results of the investigation with accuracy. You will need to:

1 create a pie chart, with a key to represent each group of data

2 draw a bar chart to represent the values of the different groups of data

3 draw a pictogram that represents each group of data using a suitable symbol for the values

4 write a review of the graphical methods used, stating which is most effective for the data and why.

Discuss with your partner.

Types of graph

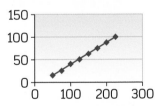

■ Figure 3.5: Line graph

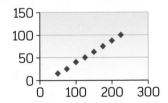

■ Figure 3.6: Scatter graph

Line graphs, as shown in Figure 3.5, are useful for showing how things change over a period of time or where one value is being compared to another – for example, the extension of a spring relative to the load applied or the distance travelled as a function of time.

Scatter graphs, as shown in Figure 3.6, can be useful if you are collecting lots of measurements from an investigation. A scatter graph can be used to produce a line of best fit. Scatter graphs and lines of best fit are covered in the next lesson.

Remember, when you are deciding on the type of chart or graph to use, think about the following questions.

- How many groups of data are there?
- What do you want the chart or graph to show?
- What is the information going to be used for?

CHECK MY LEARNING

You have looked at the types of graph and chart that can be used to present data.

Using some examples of charts and graphs, discuss as a class group why each type of graph/chart was chosen to present that data, and which methods are most effective.

Displaying data using lines of best fit

So far, we have looked at data that:
- can be sorted into groups
- follow a trend or pattern.

Unfortunately, when we carry out investigations into how a material or component reacts to different conditions, the data often cannot easily be grouped or presented as perfect straight-line graphs.

To ensure that the data from an investigation is valid, the same test is often repeated. This means that there will be a number of different values for each test (see, for example, Table 3.4), and these values are best presented using a scatter graph.

Scatter graphs

Once you have created a scatter graph (see, for example, Figure 3.7), the results are presented visually, but they are not always very effective at communicating information. For example, it is difficult to identify trends or patterns that might be useful or conclusive to the extent you require when investigating an engineered component or material.

◻ **Table 3.4: Example of data from a practical investigation**

Mass (g)	Length (mm)				
	Test 1	Test 2	Test 3	Test 4	Test 5
50	10	12	11	8	10
100	14	15	13	17	15
150	19	20	21	21	19
200	26	25	27	24	26
250	32	30	29	30	28
300	34	35	37	33	35

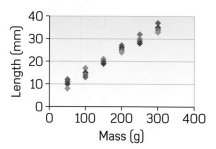

◻ **Figure 3.7: Scatter graph for the data in Table 3.4**

Lines and curves of best fit

When you look at the scatter graph in Figure 3.7, the large number of individual points plotted can be difficult to interpret. To make it easier to understand the message a scatter graph is trying to tell us, we use the plotted data to draw a line of best fit.

A line or curve of best fit can pass through some of the plotted points, sometimes most of them, or sometimes none of them! A line of best fit can also help to identify values that have been measured incorrectly.

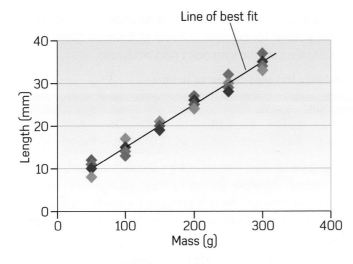

□ **Figure 3.8: Line of best fit for the information in Table 3.4**

As you can see in Figure 3.8, drawing a line of best fit shows that there is a straight-line relationship between the load and the length of the extended spring.

When plotting a graph, you need to ensure that you use the most precise scale that you can, using graph paper with 1 mm or 2 mm squares if possible. Draw your *x*-axis and *y*-axis clearly. Normally, times would be on the *x*-axis and distances would be on the *y*-axis.

Make sure you **label** the axes of your charts and graphs clearly to indicate what is being shown.

It is important to use your observational skills when looking at the data/results of practical activities; it could be that one of the measurements you made was inaccurate or a component was faulty. This will be covered in more detail in the next lesson.

KEY TERM

Labelling should be used to identify groups of data clearly.

CHECK MY LEARNING

You carried out an activity to collect some data from a spring load–extension experiment. Take the scatter graph you produced and try to draw a line of best fit. What do the results show you?

With a partner, think about and discuss the reasons why tabulated data and scatter graphs are useful in engineering investigations.

Interpretation of data

GETTING STARTED

Look at some examples of tabulated data. With a partner, discuss what you each think the data is telling you. Do you and your partner have the same opinion or interpretation?

When you look at a table of data, it is not always obvious what information the data are telling us, especially if the categories that the data is divided into are not equal. It is important, however, that we are able to interpret and understand the data so that we can use it to help design or redesign engineered components or products.

Comparison of trends and patterns

Sometimes a table of data alone can be enough to allow us to compare results and identify a trend or pattern; for example, in Table 3.5 it can be clearly seen that as time increases, the distance from the start point also increases.

◘ **Table 3.5: Distance travelled compared to time**

Distance–time comparison								
Time (seconds)	0	5	10	15	20	25	30	35
Distance (metres)	0	10	20	30	40	50	60	70

The data in Table 3.5 also show that for every 5 seconds of travel, the distance increases by 10 metres. Therefore, we have a linear (straight-line) relationship between distance and time, and there is probably no need to draw this as a graph. Sometimes, however, the results of an investigation can be harder to interpret as patterns may not be so clear.

ACTIVITY

Find a table of data from the internet (or obtain one from your teacher). Make sure that there are around ten rows in the table; this should be enough to identify a pattern.

1   Look at the data in the table. Can you see a trend or pattern? Write down your initial thoughts.

2   Plot the data on a scatter graph and draw a line of best fit.

3   Compare the graph with your initial thoughts. Did you successfully identify the trend?

V (V)	I (A)
0.00	0.00
1.50	0.40
3.00	0.78
4.50	1.00
6.00	1.15
7.50	1.28
9.00	1.42
12.00	1.62

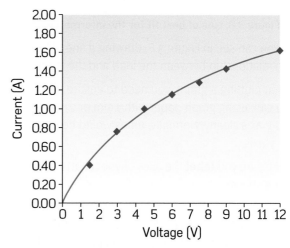

◘ **Figure 3.9: Table and chart showing current measured against voltage**

In the table in Figure 3.9, you can see that as the voltage (V) increases, the current (I) also increases, but the rate of increase is not constant or linear. This tells us that we would not get a straight-line graph. The graph in Figure 3.9 shows all of the points plotted as a scatter graph with a curved line of best fit. The line indicates that there is a trend: as the voltage increases, the current increases but the rate of increase becomes slightly less.

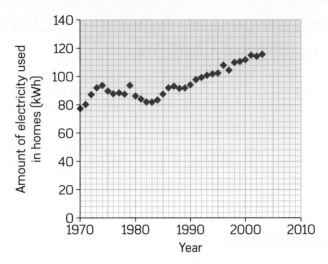

□ **Figure 3.10:** Scatter graph showing the use of electricity in homes

Figure 3.10, even though the values do not show an exact pattern, indicates that there is an upward (increasing) trend over a period of time. It would be possible to draw a line of best fit from the value in 1970 to the value in 2004, but this would not be an accurate representation of the information. This graph also shows an example of an anomalous result, which can be seen for the year 1979, where there was a large increase in the use of electricity compared with the years before and after.

Identifying anomalous results and sources of error

An anomalous result is one that does not fit the expected pattern or trend. Usually when we are carrying out an investigation, an anomalous result is caused by a mistake in taking readings or a faulty sample. To remove the possibility of anomalous results causing problems in an investigation, we take more than one reading for each value, as we did with the loaded spring investigation. This helps us to identify errors and find the possible sources such as, for example, an inaccurate measurement or a component with a flaw. It can be difficult to identify anomalous results in a table of data; however, when the data is presented in a scatter graph, they are easier to identify. In the scatter graph in Figure 3.11, anomalous results are circled.

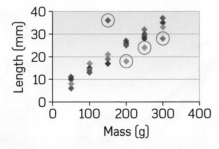

□ **Figure 3.11:** Scatter graph with anomalous results identified

CHECK MY LEARNING

You have learned about the comparison of trends and patterns in data and about the identification of anomalous results from investigations, as well as the potential causes of these results. With a partner, examine some scatter graphs from practical investigations and see if you can identify any anomalous results.

Evaluating processes, drawing conclusions and making recommendations

We have previously looked at how data can be collected and presented. The next stage is to interpret and analyse the data and use the results to recommend improvements to a product or process.

Data can be used for a range of purposes, including finding out how components perform, checking the properties of materials, and determining whether parts will fit together. You can collect such data using a range of methods, including the use of measuring equipment and gauges.

Measuring equipment

Depending on what you need to measure, you will use a range of measuring equipment. Some examples are shown in Table 3.6.

■ **Table 3.6: Types of measuring equipment**

Measurement	Equipment
Length/diameter	• Ruler: used for measuring lengths to a precision of 1mm
	• Vernier callipers: used to measure the length or diameter of smaller components, to a precision of 0.02 mm. Vernier callipers are used for very accurate measurements
	• Micrometer: used to measure the dimensions of small components to a precision of 0.001 mm
	• Tape measure: used for larger length measurements
Mass	• Balance: used to measure the mass of an object, e.g. beam balances for large masses and digital balances for smaller masses
Time	• Stopwatch: used to measure time, to a precision of 0.01 seconds. (In reality, accuracy depends on the person operating the stopwatch.)
	• Electronic systems: automatically start and stop when a sensor is actuated and are more accurate

■ **A range of measuring equipment is usually needed to check components and parts**

Sometimes it is not necessary to measure the exact size of a component. For instance, you may simply need to know whether a component and any of its features are correct, such as whether a drilled hole has a large enough diameter. To carry out checks like this, you could use a simple gauge.

Gauges

Gauges provide a simple method of checking whether or not a component or part is fit for purpose and is within tolerance. One of the most common types of gauge for engineering activities is a go/no-go gauge.

Go/no-go gauges can be used for checking the diameters of holes.
- The 'go' gauge, coloured green, must be able to fit through the hole. If the 'go' gauge does not fit, the hole is too small. This would tell us that the hole needs to be drilled larger.
- If the 'no-go' gauge, coloured red, fits through the hole, this means the hole is too large and a smaller drill bit should have been used.
- If the hole is within tolerance, the 'go' gauge will fit in the hole and the 'no-go' gauge will not.

Measuring equipment and gauges can be used to check the lengths of components, the thicknesses of materials or the overall dimensions of a part. If parts are separated into those that are too small, those that are within tolerance, and those that are too big, then it will be easier to identify the causes of faults. This can help you to draw conclusions from the data.

In an engineering workshop where more than one person is making parts, it could be that a machine has been set up incorrectly or the wrong materials have been used. You can collect and analyse data and use the conclusions drawn to make recommendations to improve manufacturing processes.

ACTIVITY

Working with a partner, check the accuracy of a sample of parts. For this, you need a go/no-go gauge and components created using engineering tools. Check the lengths of the components and divide them into categories of 'too small', 'too big' and 'within tolerance'.

Write down the reasons why you think the components were either 'too small' or 'too big'.

CHECK MY LEARNING

You have looked at different methods of making and using measurements.

With your partner, think about how measured data can be used to make recommendations to improve manufacturing processes and outcomes.

Learning aim A: assessment practice

How you will be assessed

In this component, you will be assessed by completing a set task that consists of two parts, worth 60 marks in total. The task will be set and marked by Pearson examiners, and you will complete both parts of the assessment during a period of one week. You will be supervised during the assessment period, and you will have two hours for Part 1 and one and a half hours for Part 2.

For Part 1 of the set task, you will need to carry out a practical activity and then complete a task and answer booklet. You will be given a brief with all the necessary information you need to carry out the practical task, including a table in which to record your results and observations. These results are important as you will need to refer to them when carrying out the practical activities.

You will then carry out three activities based on the practical task. An additional task, consisting of two activities, will target higher-order planning, redesign and evaluation skills, and will relate to given scenarios. During the set task, you will need to show that you understand how to interpret information and use this to suggest improvements to an engineered product.

Note: You must always observe safe practices when carrying out practical activities.

Remember that the examiner who will be marking your set task does not know you, and the only way they will be able to assess your engineering skills is through the work that they see you have completed.

CHECKPOINT

Strengthen
- Describe four methods of presenting data graphically.
- Give an example of one type of work instruction and what it is used for.
- Which methods can be used to improve an engineered product?

Challenge
- Explain why an engineer might use a gauge when carrying out quality checks.
- Describe two advantages of using mechanical fixings for engineering products.
- Explain what should be done if data show anomalous results.

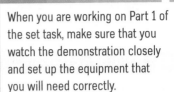

ASSESSMENT ACTIVITY   LEARNING AIM   A

You will be given information about how to prepare for and set up your investigation.

A scenario will be given to you, along with a list of the equipment that you will need.

Your teacher will demonstrate how you need to carry out the investigation, and then you will complete the set task on your own.

TAKE IT FURTHER

Check that you have set up the equipment correctly and that you have recorded values with accuracy. Try to identify any patterns or trends in the data you have collected.

TIP

When you are working on Part 1 of the set task, make sure that you watch the demonstration closely and set up the equipment that you will need correctly.

Interpretation of a given brief for an engineered product

When designing engineered products, it is important that you can interpret a design brief and then explore design ideas that provide a solution to the brief. To do this, you need to understand the information included in the design brief and know how to address each point of the brief in your designs.

Analysing the existing product with reference to the design brief

■ All products, from a simple coat hook to an aeroplane engine, are produced from a design brief

A design brief for an engineering product will include a range of factors, including:

● physical requirements
● aesthetics
● size
● function
● performance requirements.

The amount of information for each factor will vary depending on the type of product. For example, a component that is going to fit inside an engine will probably have fewer aesthetic requirements than it has performance requirements.

Physical requirements

Does the design need to meet any specific physical requirements? Will the component need to be able to hold a specific loading or be connected to another component in a specific way?

Does the component need to offer any form of protection to other components or features? Do the materials used for the component need to perform in any specific way?

Aesthetics

You will need to think about why the product is shaped in the way that it is. Is the component designed in a specific shape and style for a particular reason, or simply to make it look good?

Size

How big does the component or product need to be? Are there any maximum or minimum size requirements for the product?

You might be designing a component that is going to be a direct replacement for something that already exists. In this case, the size of the new component will be the same as the current one.

Function

You need to think about what the product or component is designed to do. This could be a list of statements. For example, a light switch must control electrical current to a light fitting and must also enclose all the wires and prevent the user from getting an electric shock. In lots of cases, there will be an overlap with performance requirements.

Performance requirements

You need to think about how the success of the product is measured. Does it need to last for a set time or be able to move a specified distance? Performance requirements will be different for each product, but they can often be thought of as targets that need to be met for the product or component to be termed a success.

ACTIVITY

Research an engineered product, either by looking on the internet or by examining a physical product.

Write out a design brief for the product. You need to include the following:

1 physical requirements

2 aesthetics

3 size

4 function

5 performance requirements.

Exchange your design brief with a partner and see if they can identify what the product is just from the description in the brief.

CHECK MY LEARNING

In this lesson, you have analysed an existing engineered product with reference to its design brief.

Working with a partner, analyse one product that is in your workshop or classroom and write a design brief for the product.

Features of engineered products

When you are investigating an existing engineered product to help with the design of something new, you will need to consider the features of the product. There are different types of feature that products can have.

ACTIVITY

Working with your partner, research an example of a fabricated component.

1 Sketch the component.

2 Label the features of the component.

3 Highlight the features of the component that you think are most important for it to work as intended.

Dimensions

The dimensions of a product are very important. If a dimension is too big, it will probably not fit in the space it is designed for; if it is too small, then connections to other components will not be possible. This is known as tolerance, which can be linear (straight-line) or radial (for circular features).

When you examine a product to check its dimensions, you will use one of the following measuring tools.

- Steel rule – steel rules are used for measuring lengths to a precision of 1 mm.
- Micrometer – these can be used to find the dimensions of small components to a precision of 0.001 mm.
- Vernier callipers – these are used to measure the length or diameter of smaller components to a precision of 0.02 mm. Vernier callipers are used for very accurate measurements.
- Tape measure – these are used for larger dimensions where precision is less important.

When you are selecting measuring equipment to collect data, you need to think about the following points.

- How precise do the measurements need to be?
- How many measurements will you need to take?
- What is the reason for taking the measurements?
- The size and shape of the component to be measured.

You should always record length measurements in millimetres (mm).

Tolerances

For component parts of an engineered product to fit together properly, they need to be produced to an agreed tolerance. Sometimes there are slight variations in the sizes or positions of features when components are made. Providing these are within tolerance, the parts will fit together and work as intended.

Surface finishes

The surface finish of an object says how smooth its surface is. Surface finish is measured in micrometres (μm). 1 μm = 0.0000001 m.

The finish applied to the component will have a significant impact on how the component looks, but will also influence how resistant the component will be to wear and damage, or to corrosion, e.g. rust. As with dimensions, there are tolerances for surface finish – for example, how smooth a feature must be or how thick a paint finish should be.

◨ **Many different surface finishes can be applied to materials to change their appearance**

Physical form

The physical form of a component is the shape it takes. Try to be descriptive about the form of an object; think about whether it is a regular shape, such as a cone, cube or cylinder, or an abstract shape that is harder to describe. Consider using terms such as 2D, 3D, flat and curved to support your descriptions.

Try to describe the form using a combination of shapes. In the case of the component in the photograph, a description could be that it has a long rectangular body that is connected to an approximately square plate with a hole in its centre.

Consider other physical attributes that might cause problems, such as injury from impacting sharp corners or moisture traps in which water could collect and damage the product.

CHECK MY LEARNING

You have learned about the types of feature an engineered product can have. In your class group, discuss what you understand by tolerances and the importance of these for engineered products.

Selecting engineering materials

GETTING STARTED

Write down as many examples of materials as you can think of for each of the following material categories: ferrous and non-ferrous metals, and thermosetting and thermoforming polymers.

LINK IT UP

To remind yourself of the range of engineering materials used in manufacturing engineered components and products, go back to Component 2: Learning aim A.

Most of the materials you will encounter when investigating existing solutions will be similar to the four material categories that you have already covered.

Categories of material

The following is a review of the general properties and characteristics of each material group and how these influence material choices.

Ferrous metals

Ferrous metals contain iron. Ferrous metal alloys also contain other metals to give them the properties required. For example, stainless steel is corrosion resistant because it contains other metals such as chromium and nickel (see Table 3.7).

▣ Table 3.7: Examples of ferrous metals

Material	Properties
Mild steel	• Good tensile strength • Good levels of malleability and ductility
Stainless steel	• Very tough • Corrosion resistant
Wrought iron	• Very tough • Corrosion resistant • Good levels of malleability and ductility

Non-ferrous metals

Non-ferrous metals do not contain iron. Unlike ferrous metals, they are not magnetic and usually have better corrosion resistance (see Table 3.8).

▣ Table 3.8: Examples of non-ferrous metals

Material	Properties
Aluminium	• Soft and malleable • Good conductor of heat and electricity • Corrosion resistant
Titanium	• Low density • Quite good levels of ductility
Copper	• Tough material • Very ductile • Very good electrical conductor

Thermosetting polymers

Thermosetting polymers have a rigid molecular structure that is made up of lines of molecules that are heavily cross-linked. They can be heated and shaped once, but they cannot be reshaped, because they become permanently stiff and solid after being heat treated (see Table 3.9).

◼ Table 3.9: Examples of thermosetting polymers

Material	Properties
Phenol-formaldehyde	• High electrical resistance • High heat resistance • Hard wearing
Polyimides	• Hard and tough with good rigidity • Self-lubricating • Resistant to oil, fuels and chemicals
Polyurethane	• Good hardness properties • High tensile and compression strength • Impact and abrasion resistant

Thermoforming polymers

Thermoforming polymers have fewer cross-links than thermosetting polymers. This means that when they are heated they become soft and can be formed into a variety of shapes and forms. When they cool, they become stiff and solid again. However, the process can be repeated many times (see Table 3.10).

◼ Table 3.10: Examples of thermoforming polymers

Material	Properties
Polyethylene	• Excellent chemical resistance • Good fatigue and wear resistance
Polypropylene	• Quite high tensile strength • Good resistance to stress and cracking
Acrylic	• Very stiff material • Good durability • Good electrical insulator

ACTIVITY

Find an example of an engineered product (from the internet or from your teacher) and examine the product to identify the materials used to make it.

1 Name all materials used in the product and what they are used for.

2 Research the properties of these materials.

3 Suggest alternative materials that have similar properties to the existing materials.

CHECK MY LEARNING

You have learned about the properties of some of the materials used in engineered products.

In a small group, discuss and explain the reasons why you chose the alternative materials for the engineered product you looked at in the main lesson activity.

Manufacturing processes

GETTING STARTED

Working in groups, disassemble an engineered product. Write a list of the processes that you think have been used in the manufacture of the product.

LINK IT UP

Go to Component 1: Learning aim B and Component 2: Learning aim A to review processes used in manufacturing.

When an engineered product is manufactured, a range of processes, generally divided into four groups, is used to make sure that it is produced to the highest possible standard.

Cutting processes

Cutting involves the removal of unwanted material. Sometimes you are left with more than one piece, such as when you use a saw. Other processes only leave swarf or filings, such as drilling and filing. Table 3.11 lists some examples of cutting processes.

■ Table 3.11: Examples of cutting processes

Process	Examples of use
Drilling	• Making holes through a material • Counterboring to allow components to sit below the surface of a workpiece • Producing blind holes and flat-bottomed holes that do not go all the way through material
Sawing	• Mechanical or manual methods can be used • Hacksaws are generally used for metallic materials and have different blade types for different thicknesses of metal • Coping saws can be used for cutting many polymers
Filing	• Used to remove burrs or sharp edges from the surface of metal • Can be used to add a round edge or chamfer to a cut material • Can be used to make holes bigger or to shape them to specification
Shearing	• Used to produce straight cuts • Can be used on sheet material or bar and angle stock

Shaping processes

Shaping processes are most often used with metals. They involve using cutting tools to remove material and produce the shape of the component required by the design. Table 3.12 lists some examples of shaping processes.

■ Table 3.12: Examples of shaping processes

Process	Examples of use
Turning	• Producing flat faces that are a square end to a bar • Producing a range of diameters on bars, including parallel, stepped and tapered • Adding features to the outside of a bar, including screw threads, knurling and chamfers
Milling	• Producing flat, square and parallel features • Machining shoulders, steps, slots, grooves and recesses

Forming processes

Forming processes often involve the use of heat, changing materials from one form to another. For example, polymer pellets are first heated and then injection moulded to form products. Table 3.13 lists some examples of forming processes.

◘ Table 3.13: Examples of forming processes

Process	Examples of use
Casting	• Sand casting is used for large components, where dimensional accuracy is less important • Die casting is used for large batches and where tolerances are tight • Investment casting is used for very complex shapes, where dimensional tolerances are very important
Forging	• Drop forging is used for smaller shapes, where production rates are high • Upset forging is used for simple products, such as the head of a bolt • Press forging is used for large objects
Extruding	• Extruding is a process used for polymers. Complicated hollow sections can be made by forcing soft polymers through a die
Moulding	• Injection moulding is used for complex shapes, such as housings for electronics • Blow moulding is used for hollow containers, such as bottles • Vacuum forming is used for simple hollow containers and enclosures

Joining and fabrication processes

Once component parts have been manufactured, they need to be joined together. These joining processes can be permanent or temporary and may depend, for example, on whether maintenance requires the parts to be taken apart. Table 3.14 lists some examples of joining processes.

◘ Table 3.14: Examples of joining processes

Process	Examples of use
Fastening	• Fastenings provide a mechanical joint between components. Most are temporary, e.g. screws, nuts, bolts and clips • Permanent fasteners include rivets
Bonding	• Bonding is similar to gluing, giving an adhesive joint between materials • Factors that influence the strength of bonding include the pressure applied, the materials to be joined and the temperature
Soldering	• This process is used for joining electronic components to circuit boards • A soldering iron is used to melt solder, which solidifies to make the joint
Brazing	• A process similar to soldering but at a much higher temperature • Used to join different metals together, e.g. in heating systems

ACTIVITY

Examine an engineered product and investigate the manufacturing processes used to make it.

1 Name all of the processes used to manufacture the product.

2 Research two contrasting production processes – for example, one forming and one joining.

3 Create a short presentation that describes the two processes.

CHECK MY LEARNING ◼ ◻ ◻

As covered in this lesson and in Components 1 and 2, different types of manufacturing process can be used. In a small group, discuss the different options that can be used to manufacture an engineered product.

Redesign

Before you begin to think about ways in which you can redesign an existing product, you need to identify any issues there are with the existing design.

Identifying issues with existing designs

This is an important part of the engineering design process and often involves asking questions such as:

- Are the existing materials suitable?
- Has the product been manufactured using the most suitable processes?
- Are there any weak points in the design?
- Is the product too complicated – how many parts are used in the assembly?
- Does the product make the most efficient use of materials?

Issues may be identified during the design stage, while prototyping or testing, or by the end user over a period of operation of the product. When trying to identify issues with an existing design, you should refer to and consider the original design brief for the product.

Once you have identified potential issues with an existing design, you can then start to look at methods to develop and share your redesign ideas.

Concept 2D sketching

One of the first steps is to produce some sketched ideas. Usually, this involves drawing 2D sketches that show the design proposal from one view only.

There are no right or wrong approaches; the only limit is your creativity.

Practising sketching

To develop your sketching techniques, you need to practise making sketches of a variety of objects and design ideas. Remember to include **annotations** to explain the features of your designs. Annotations can provide information about:

- materials
- processes
- dimensions.

Annotations will help others to understand your design thinking and will also help to explain how something is to be made or the reasons why a particular material is to be used.

KEY TERM

Annotations are labels used by engineers to give information about designs.

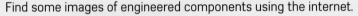

ACTIVITY

Find some images of engineered components using the internet.

1 Print out images of the components.

2 Sketch out the components using only 2D views.

3 Add annotations to the sketches to explain the different features of the components.

When you are producing 2D annotated sketches, you should think about:

- which view will show the most information about the component
- what information needs to be explained in the annotations
- making sure that sketches are large enough to show all the details you want to share.

CHECK MY LEARNING

You have looked at ways of identifying issues with existing designs and practised sketching techniques that you can use to explain the features of products you are designing.

In pairs, evaluate the sketches you made in the previous activity and discuss how effective sketches are at representing given components.

3D sketching

There are limitations on the amount of information that can be shown by 2D drawings. To show all the features of a component, you might need to produce at least three different 2D sketches. Another way is to use 3D sketches to represent three-dimensional objects.

Using 3D sketching

There are three methods of 3D sketching that are often used as part of the design process. These are oblique and isometric projections and perspective drawings.

Oblique projection

With an oblique projection, you draw one full face of an object or component. This is drawn either full size or to scale. Lines are then projected back at 45° from the corners to show the depth of the object. Sometimes these lines are drawn full size (or to scale), although it is common for them to be drawn at around half their length so that the proportions of the drawing look correct. The example in Figure 3.13 is a scaled oblique projection.

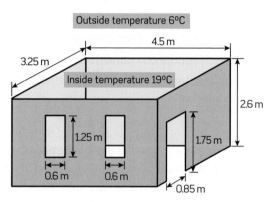

◪ Figure 3.13: Oblique projection

Isometric projection

Unlike an oblique projection, an isometric projection has all the sides drawn at an angle. Vertical lines always remain vertical. However, all horizontal lines are drawn at 30° to the horizontal, as can be seen in the example shown in Figure 3.14. Isometric drawings are good for showing how things fit together, as in **assembly drawings**, and dimensions are either drawn full size or scaled. One of the disadvantages of isometric drawings is that circles appear as ellipses and curved edges can be hard to draw.

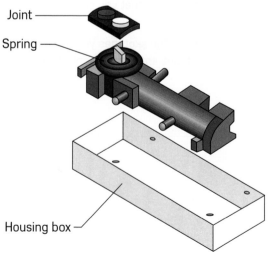

◪ Figure 3.14: Isometric projection

Perspective drawings

There are three types of perspective drawing: one-point, two-point and three-point perspectives. One-point perspective is similar to an oblique projection, with a front face being drawn in full. Two-point perspective is probably the most useful representation method, as it can be drawn to show whichever features of the component need to be emphasised. As with isometric projections, vertical lines remain vertical, but all horizontal lines project to **vanishing points**, as shown in Figure 3.15.

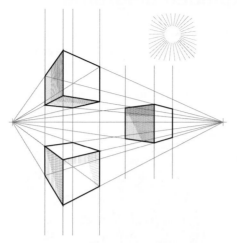

■ Figure 3.15: Two-point perspective drawing

Table 3.15 lists some advantages and disadvantages of these 3D drawing types.

■ Table 3.15: Advantages and disadvantages of the 3D drawing types

3D drawing type	Advantages	Disadvantages
Oblique projection	• Gives an accurate view of one face • Gives an impression of depth or thickness of components • Measurements can be taken from the front face	• Circles are shown as ellipses except on the front face • The component can look distorted due to the perspective
Isometric projection	• Shows three sides of a component clearly • No changes to the proportions of the drawing • Easy to interpret by most people	• Can be hard to add dimensions or take measurements from • Circles are drawn as ellipses
Perspective drawing	• Gives a realistic view of the product or component • Allows the component to be shown from any angle	• Due to the perspective, some details may be hard to see • Difficult to add dimensions • Circles and curved edges are hard to show

ACTIVITY

Select some simple engineered components. Sketch them using each of the three techniques: oblique projection, isometric projection and perspective drawings.

CHECK MY LEARNING

You have learned about the differences between three types of 3D sketch commonly used in engineering. In a small group, discuss which of the three methods you think shows an engineered product most realistically.

Exploded diagrams

Although 3D sketches are useful for showing how an engineered product looks when it is completed, they have limited use when you want to explain how the individual parts of a product fit together.

Exploded diagrams are usually drawn as isometric projections that show each of the individual parts and how they are joined together to produce the finished product.

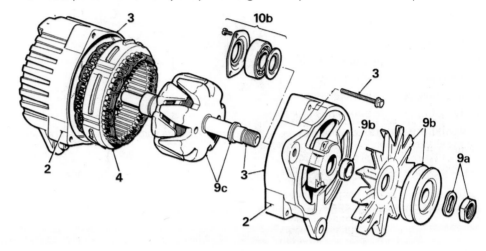

▣ **Figure 3.16: An exploded diagram of a an alternator.**

When producing an exploded diagram, there are some guidelines that should be followed:

● Parts should always line up with each other, to show exactly how they fit together in the finished product.
● Parts should be easy to identify, using either the part names or a reference number system (as in the alternator drawing in Figure 3.16).
● If a part cannot be shown in line with where it fits into the assembly, add projection lines to show where the part needs to be placed. This can be seen for the component parts numbered 10b in Figure 3.16.

One of the main advantages of an exploded diagram is that each of the parts can be shown in full, and components that are inside the assembled product can be seen – for example, parts 9c and 10b in the water pump assembly.

Labelling and annotations

When you produce an exploded diagram, it is important that you clearly identify the individual components so that someone else can understand the diagram. However, this also depends on the purpose of the diagram. For example, if you are producing the diagram to explain what the parts are (as shown in Figure 3.17) and/or what they do, then you could use annotations that are detailed or name the individual parts.

If the purpose of the diagram is to provide instructions, then using a number or letter reference system would be more effective as this will make the diagram easier to understand. If you use this method, you will also need to provide a parts list.

Parts lists

Parts lists are documents used to provide information about the individual parts or components used in a product. They will usually feature:

- the reference number used in the exploded diagram
- the component's identifiable part number
- the component's description
- information on the component's materials
- quantities of each component.

Parts lists, like the one shown in Figure 3.18, are also sometimes known as a bill of materials.

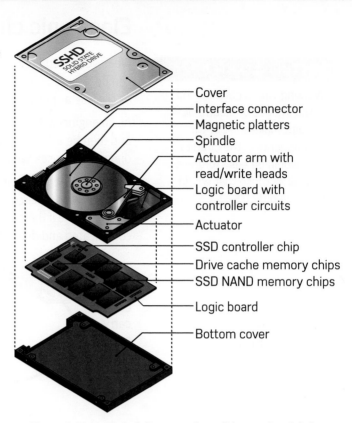

Figure 3.17: Exploded diagram of a solid state hard disk

12	6	BOLT1	BOLT	STEEL
11	4	5MM SCREW1	SCREW	STEEL
10	6	WASHER1	WASHER	COPPER
9	1	SHIELD1	SHIELD	STAINLESS STEEL
8	1	GEAR2	GEAR2, BEVEL	STAINLESS STEEL
7	1	GEAR1	GEAR1, BEVEL	STAINLESS STEEL
6	1	FLANGE2	FLANGE	STEEL
5	2	2MM SCREW1	SCREW	STEEL
4	1	SHAFT1	SHAFT, INPUT	STEEL
3	1	BASE1	BASE	STEEL
2	2	PLATE2	PLATE, OUTPUT	STAINLESS STEEL
1	1	HEAD1	HEAD, GRINDER	ALUMINIUM
FIND NO.	QTY	PART NUMBER	DESCRIPTION	MATERIAL
			HEAD ASSY, GRINDER	

Figure 3.18: Typical parts list

Electronic circuit diagrams

GETTING STARTED

Working with a partner, find some images of electronic circuits. Make a list of the components in the circuits that would be easy to draw, as well as those that would be more difficult.

We have looked previously at ways in which engineered products and components can be drawn, using methods and techniques that make the drawings and diagrams as realistic as possible and easy to understand.

As an engineer, it is very unusual to be given a pictorial drawing of an electronic circuit and then be asked to manufacture it. It is more usual for you to be given a circuit diagram that uses symbols to represent components.

Compare the two drawings shown in Figures 3.19 and 3.20, which both represent a simple electronic circuit consisting of one battery cell, one resistor and one light bulb. Now, imagine if there were 20 or 30 components in the circuit – how much more complicated and difficult to understand would a pictorial drawing be?

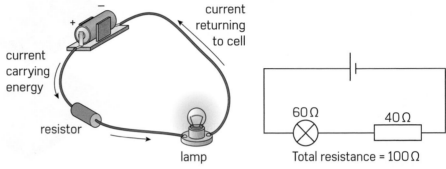

◼ Figure 3.19: Pictorial drawing of a circuit

◼ Figure 3.20: Schematic diagram of the circuit

Things would be even more complicated if the circuit were manufactured using a printed circuit board (PCB) that contained resistors, capacitors, integrated circuits and transistors. In a circuit schematic diagram, each of these components has a specific symbol to represent it.

◼ Electronic components on a PCB

Electronic component symbols

Electronics engineers use a range of symbols to represent each type of electronic component that can be used in an electronic circuit.

ACTIVITY

Use the internet to research the symbols used for a range of electronic components. Create a table that includes:

1 the description/name of each component

2 an image of the actual electronic component

3 the electronic circuit schematic symbol for the component.

When you draw a circuit schematic diagram, it needs to meet international design standards; so you must use the correct symbols. It should be possible for anyone who understands circuit schematic diagrams to manufacture the circuit from the schematic diagram.

When you are drawing an electronic circuit schematic diagram, you should:

- use straight horizontal and vertical lines
- draw all component symbols at the same scale
- avoid having symbols too close together, making sure that it is clear how the different components are connected.

CHECK MY LEARNING

You have learned how to produce circuit schematic diagrams using the correct circuit symbols.

1 Collect images, or physical examples, of some electronic circuits.

2 Draw the circuit schematic diagram for each circuit.

3 Produce a parts list of the components in the circuits.

Design for manufacture

While designers who develop concepts for new mobile phones or for cars consider mostly how the product will look or the features it will have, engineers who plan the manufacture of the product need to be able to interpret designs and identify the most appropriate materials, processes and tools required to produce the necessary parts.

□ **Prototype design for a sports car**

KEY TERMS

Chamfers are features that remove sharp corners to make something safer and easier to assemble.
Radius (or **radii**) refers to a smooth, rounded corner, like a chamfer, typically used on external corners.

When you are redesigning a product or component, it is important that you consider how it will be made and assembled. For example, if two parts of a product need to be joined together with pins, then it would be helpful for the assembly process if a **chamfer** or **radius** is added to both the pins and the holes through which the pins will pass.

Design approaches

There are different approaches that can be used when designing for manufacture:
- reduce the number of parts
- design components for assembly
- use standard sizes and fixings
- avoid sharp corners.

Other approaches can be used, but for the majority of simple engineered products, the above design approaches are likely to achieve the best improvements to a design.

Reduce the number of parts

If possible, reduce the number of parts, which will probably reduce both the weight and the amount of material used. Components fabricated from individual parts could possibly be cast or moulded in one piece. This removes the need for fixings and allows components to be manufactured more efficiently.

Design components for assembly

Removing the possibility of mistakes occurring during assembly is one way to improve any product. Designing components so that it is only possible to assemble them in the correct way will help prevent faulty products being made, which is especially important when considering the time and effort associated with producing machined components.

Designing components for assembly allows semi-skilled workers to put products together. This is also important for self-assembly products that have components that need to be finally assembled by end users and where mistakes during assembly could easily damage the product.

Use standard sizes and fixings

Redesign a product to use popular standard sizes of components and fixings that are more readily available. This will eliminate the need to design and make new fixings. It should also allow product end users to carry out equipment repairs themselves.

It is also a good idea to use only a small range of types and sizes of mechanical fixing and to avoid using smaller sizes as much as possible, all of which will make fabrication less complicated.

Avoid sharp corners

When you design an engineered product, you need to ensure that it will perform as you expect it to. One way of doing this is to ensure that you avoid sharp corners and edges as much as possible by using generous **fillets** or radii to produce a smooth transition from one face of the component to another. Sometimes you cannot avoid a sharp corner, such as, with a fabricated container. However, for cast, forged or formed components, adding radii can make a component less likely to fail in service.

KEY TERM

Fillets are similar to radii, but feature on internal corners and are used to reduce stresses in a joint.

ACTIVITY

Find an example of an engineered product that is made from two or three components that fit together.

1 Disassemble the product.

2 Identify one component that you think could be improved, which will improve the overall product.

3 Sketch two or three improvements to the design of the component.

4 Explain how the component would be manufactured to the improved design.

When complete, compare your ideas with those of a partner.

CHECK MY LEARNING

You have learned about some of the methods used to improve the design of a product and allow it to be manufactured more efficiently.

In a small group, investigate some engineered products. Discuss ways in which the product could be improved to make it easier to manufacture.

Variations in form to solve a problem

GETTING STARTED

Look around the room you are working in. How many products have a variety of forms, yet perform the same function (e.g. different models of mobile phone)? Make a list of the features that the product designs have in common with each other.

An engineering design brief is produced to make sure that new products perform the function they are intended to do. However, this does not mean that there is only one approach that can be taken to solve the design problem.

It is important to ensure that each of the criteria in the design brief and product design specification is met, but how this is achieved could be very varied.

Imagine a design brief that asks you to come up with a solution to the problem of fixing a camera to the handlebars of a bicycle. Possible approaches could include:
- a bracket that is welded to the handlebars
- a removable case attached using a clamp
- clips that allow the camera to be easily fixed/removed.

◻ **Examples of a desktop and a laptop computer**

Consider two examples of computer shown in the photographs. While both perform the same function, the way in which this is achieved is quite different. The laptop computer is more versatile, as it can be transported from one place to another, allowing someone to work on the move. The desktop computer can be fitted with multiple hard drives and interfaces, thus allowing the user to be more productive.

ACTIVITY

You have been asked to design an engineered product that can be used to support a portable hard disk drive when it is used with a laptop computer. You need to:

1 Research the dimensions of portable hard disk drives.

2 Research any existing products that meet the design brief.

3 Produce five or six different ideas that will meet the design criteria.

When producing design ideas for a product, you need to think about how you can change the form of the product – in other words, the shape and look of the product. Some ways of doing this include:
- swapping or substituting materials or processes for something different, perhaps to make the engineering product easier to produce
- combining features from different designs to produce a solution that makes an engineering product more useful

- adapting an existing design that fulfils a different purpose and making it suitable for the problem you are solving
- modifying the look of the design – perhaps make it tall and narrow, or short and wide, or change its shape; does it need to be a regular shape or might other shapes be more efficient?
- putting the product to another use – would the product still work if it were used for another, but similar, purpose?
- eliminating parts that are not needed – could you use fewer materials or processes, or make the product simpler, or reduce it in size and weight?
- reversing parts of the design – could you produce a solution that works in completely the opposite way but still meets the needs of the brief?

These are just some of the methods that you could use when redesigning a product. It is always important to think about how the component parts will be made and assembled.

◼ **Examples of design sketches and concepts for an engineered product**

LINK IT UP

In Component 1: Learning aim B, you created design sketches as part of a design and make process.

CHECK MY LEARNING

You have learned about how the form of an engineering product can affect how effective the product is at meeting its design brief.

As a group, produce a mind map that shows the factors an engineer should consider when changing the form of an engineered product.

Variations in approach to solve a problem

It is important to ensure that the solution chosen meets the engineering design brief, but there are many ways in which engineers can find a solution that satisfies the brief. Sometimes, the solutions can be very complex; at other times they may be quite basic. However, most of the time the solution is only as complex as it needs to be.

Example

The photographs showing stepping stones and a suspension bridge are two examples of a solution to the following design brief:

- Provide a method of crossing a river so that the users do not get wet.

▢ Stepping stones   ▢ Suspension bridge

Sometimes, a very simple solution can be found, like the solution using the stepping stones. But a simple solution may not meet all the needs of the potential users of the crossing. For example, it would be difficult for a person on a bicycle, or pushing a child in a buggy or pushing a wheelchair user, to cross the river.

Alternatively, the suspension bridge is a complex solution to the same problem. This approach allows people to cross in many ways, including using motor vehicles. The solution, however, will take a long time to construct and will also be very expensive to build.

Factors such as the overall benefits of a design, as well as the cost, time and techniques required to manufacture the proposed solution, all need to be considered carefully when selecting the most appropriate solution to meet a design brief.

ACTIVITY

Find a range of engineered products that meet the same general design requirements – for example, types of mobile phone or bicycle.

1 Research different examples of these products, each taking a different approach to solve the problem.

2 Make notes to explain how each idea meets the design requirements.

3 Sketch the parts of each design that are effective in meeting the design requirements.

Although it is possible that a range of ideas can meet a design brief, there are likely to be some aspects of a design that are more effective than others. Think again about the stepping stones and the suspension bridge: while both make it possible to cross the river without getting wet, only the bridge allows a wide range of different users to cross the river.

Rating systems

One way of measuring the effectiveness of a design is to use some form of rating system. This could be simple – for example, giving each design a mark out of 10 (or any value you choose) or using what is known as a RAG (red-amber-green) rating system. This system can be used to rate how well a design meets the design brief, using the following criteria:

- red – does not meet the brief in any way
- amber – partially meets the brief
- green – fully meets the brief.

Each individual part of the design can be RAG rated and then the results presented in graphical or tabular form (see, for example, Table 3.16).

▣ **Table 3.16: RAG ratings for four types of mobile phone**

Design	Make phone calls	Send text messages	Pocket-sized	Long battery life	Waterproof	Smash-proof screen
1						
2						
3						
4						

Using the RAG rating system, it can be easily seen that Design 1 is the best design in terms of meeting the highest number of criteria.

You can also use RAG rating systems to identify design criteria that none of the design proposals can meet. You might then consider whether these criteria could be removed, or their relevance reduced, if they are less important to the overall function of the product.

ACTIVITY

Revisit the examples of engineered products you investigated in the previous activity.

1 For each product, give a RAG rating against each of the design requirements.
2 Present the results of the RAG rating in graphical or tabular format.
3 Use the RAG ratings to decide which design meets the design brief the best.

LINK IT UP

Refer to Component 1: Learning aim B and the use of creative thinking and evaluation techniques to choose the best solution to a problem.

CHECK MY LEARNING

You have investigated methods that can be used to compare different approaches to solving a problem.

With a partner, use a RAG rating approach to evaluate and compare how two products meet their intended purpose – for example, a pencil sharpener or an item of workshop equipment.

Using different componentry

Some of the engineered products we use daily are manufactured in a variety of factories and in different locations. This means that although the final product might look the same, the actual parts used are often different from one model to another.

DID YOU KNOW?

On a visit to Europe, Henry Ford saw two examples of vans that looked almost identical. One was manufactured in Britain, the other in Germany. However, the parts used to build the vans were not interchangeable – the British version used parts with imperial measurements; the German van's parts were metric.

Sometimes engineering components can be substituted for each other without any notable change in how the product is made or how it functions.

◘ **Nuts, bolts, screws and other fixings can often be substituted**

When considering the redesign of a product, you should think about whether you can standardise the components used. For example, it is good practice to limit the range of screw heads and diameters (or sizes) of screw used. This reduces the machine tooling requirements for producing holes and, if necessary, threaded holes in components; plus there is the additional advantage of needing only a limited range of tools to assemble the product.

This approach to standardisation can be used to make manufacturing and assembly processes more efficient. Time savings achieved by reducing the number of tool changes can soon add up and allow components to be made more quickly.

ACTIVITY

For a simple engineered product, investigate the possible use of alternative components as part of a product redesign.

1 Analyse the product to see which components are used to make it.

2 Research alternative appropriate components that could be used.

3 Produce annotated sketches for some alternative designs.

There are other ways in which alternative components can be used. These include:
- manufacturing the component from a different material
- using a different manufacturing process to produce the component
- redesigning the component to reduce its weight or volume
- using common components that can be used for many different purposes
- replacing two or more components with one that can perform the same functions – this is called **parts integration**.

KEY TERM

Parts integration is the ability to combine different parts.

Parts integration has a number of benefits, including reducing the overall number of parts, lowering costs and making assembly faster.

Once you start to look at replacing components with alternatives, this often leads to discovering other aspects of a design that could be improved. Using alternative components is only one way to improve a design solution. It is usual to combine this with some of the other approaches looked at previously, such as changing the form of the design or considering design for manufacture.

When redesigning a product, you should try to do the following:
- Standardise components and use only a limited range of sizes. Try to use common components and stick to these.
- Reduce the number of tooling changes that are needed. This means that the assembly of a product can be completed more efficiently.
- Think about using the same material for as many components as possible, provided this does not make the product less effective. This can allow for material to be bought in bulk and prevents issues caused by having materials that react with each other.

LINK IT UP

In Component 2: Learning aim A you learned about different types of component, including proprietary components and standardised components.

Another method of using different componentry is to combine multiple components into one; for example, a threaded bar with a nut at both ends could replace the use of two nuts and two bolts, or a bracket could be designed with three faces to replace two angle brackets.

An approach that you could follow is to:

1 select at least two components that are joined together in some way

2 produce a few sketches to show how the components could be integrated into one part.

For electronic circuits, you could consider the use of programmable integrated circuits (PICs) to reduce the number of individual components in a circuit and make the assembly of a PCB more efficient.

CHECK MY LEARNING

You have investigated methods of reducing or improving the componentry within an engineered product. This includes standardising and/or combining components.

In pairs, discuss the approaches that could be used to improve the componentry for a given engineering problem.

Evaluation

LINK IT UP

Refer to Component 1: Learning aim B to remind yourself of the evaluation techniques that can be used.

It is very unusual for any one solution to a problem to be perfect and meet all the requirements of the design brief and the product design specification. This is where the use of evaluation techniques becomes useful. However, the evaluation of design proposals is one part of the design process that can either solve problems or create them.

Reviewing the credibility of design ideas

If you carry out a detailed evaluation of each of your design proposals, this process should allow you to choose the one idea that best meets the design specification or to develop a solution that combines the features of a range of proposals.

Making the right decisions

The reason for evaluating design proposals is to ensure that you make the correct design decisions. One method is to consider the strengths and weaknesses of designs relative to each other and against the specification. You will need to analyse your proposals and make development decisions about:
- the materials and components to be used and the effectiveness of their use
- the manufacturing processes to be used.

Analysis of ideas

Look at each of the designs you have produced, including your preferred design solution. You can take different approaches to analysing and testing the ideas, including:
- discussing the ideas with other members of the group. You should prepare a number of questions related to your specification; for example, do group members think the design proposals would function as you want them to do?
- producing a prototype to check if the design proposals will function as intended; for example, if a bracket needs to join two parts together, will it actually fit?
- being critical about the designs. You need to be honest: perhaps take the approach that you are looking at something designed by others instead of by yourself.
- comparing your ideas with those that are already available in the marketplace. Do your solutions offer improvements? If not, why not? How can the ideas be improved?
- seeking expert opinions. Perhaps ask a practising engineer, one who works for a company that manufactures similar products, for their opinions, or someone who would be making use of the product on a regular basis.

ACTIVITY

In previous lessons, you looked at generating ideas to solve an engineering problem. Now, you need to look at evaluation of these ideas. To do this:

1 Select the ideas that you think are most likely to meet the needs of the problem.

2 Sketch each idea in the form of a mind map (similar to that shown in Figure 3.21).

3 Annotate the map to explain how the idea meets specific aspects of the design brief.

When you have finished your mind maps, discuss your results with a partner. Ideally, you need to find ways of further improving the designs to see if you can satisfy more aspects of the brief.

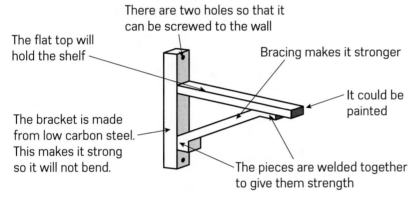

There are two holes so that it can be screwed to the wall

The flat top will hold the shelf

Bracing makes it stronger

It could be painted

The bracket is made from low carbon steel. This makes it strong so it will not bend.

The pieces are welded together to give them strength

◻ **Figure 3.21: Annotated sketch of an idea analysis**

When you are evaluating your ideas:
- Be honest – if a design brief/specification point has not been met, then say so.
- Be critical – if something can be improved, explain how it can be improved.
- Be thorough – check each specification point, looking at your ideas in depth.

CHECK MY LEARNING

You have learned about why it is necessary to review the credibility of design ideas against the requirements of a design brief.

As a group, evaluate an example of a design idea analysis produced by one member of the group. Do you all agree or disagree with the comments made by the designer?

Selecting and justifying the most appropriate design solution

When designing a solution to an engineering problem, if you have approached the process logically, you will have produced a number of ideas that all meet the design brief fully, but in different ways. It is an important part of the design process to review each idea in order to develop a solution to the problem. To some extent, you have done this previously when you produced a mind map to analyse each of your ideas. The next stage is to carry out a critical analysis of the results and then select the most appropriate solution.

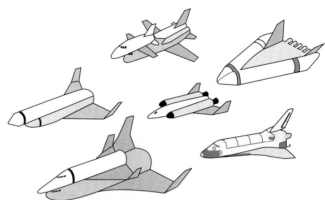

■ **Figure 3.22: Concept designs for the space shuttle**

As part of the evaluation of design ideas, you need to consider how effective each idea is at meeting the needs of the design brief and design specification. It could be that you, like NASA and many other engineering companies throughout history, will need to take elements from more than one of the design proposals you have produced and combine them into a final design.

When you are reviewing the analysis of your ideas, think about each specification point and rate ideas against individual points – think about the RAG rating approach covered in an earlier lesson. Make notes on your design work to explain how specification points are met, and think about which specification points are most important.

Justification of the design solution

When you review your ideas, it is worth looking back at the specification for the engineered product. For example, if the specification for a shelf bracket includes the points listed below, you need to think about which ones are the most important.

Specification

The shelf bracket must be able to:

1 hold a shelf that is 250 mm wide

2 support a loading of 10 kg

3 be manufactured in small batches

4 have multiple holes to allow screw fixings to be used

5 be made from durable materials

6 be finished with a range of finishes.

For a shelf bracket to do the job it is designed to do, it must meet specification points 1 and 2 fully, otherwise it will not be **fit-for-purpose**. Similarly, if point 4 is not met, then it will be difficult to fix the bracket to the wall.

In comparison, specification points 3 and 5 are not as vital for the design of the shelf bracket, but because they impact on manufacturing decisions, a solution that could not be made in batches using durable materials would be inappropriate.

Specification point 6 is more cosmetic and would generally be achieved by most designs.

When reviewing a final solution, you should explain how the specification points are met. For example, the following design proposal meets specification points 1 and 2:

- the top of the bracket is 250 mm wide and can therefore hold the shelf
- the cross member is triangulated to provide enough strength to support the load. This is welded together to provide a permanent joint.

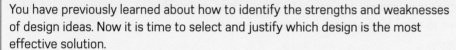

ACTIVITY

You have previously learned about how to identify the strengths and weaknesses of design ideas. Now it is time to select and justify which design is the most effective solution.

1 Use the given specification to review the effectiveness of each idea.

2 Identify the most effective solution to the problem.

3 Write a short report explaining how your chosen design meets the requirements of the specification and why you selected it as the most appropriate design.

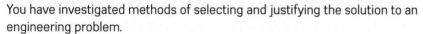

CHECK MY LEARNING

You have investigated methods of selecting and justifying the solution to an engineering problem.

As a group, discuss the approaches that should be taken when justifying the selection of an effective solution.

Justification of the processes to be used

When you produce designs to solve an engineering problem, you need to think about and justify the types of manufacturing process that should be used to manufacture the design idea.

Types of process

As we have looked at before, manufacturing processes can be grouped into the following four categories:

- cutting processes
- shaping processes
- forming processes
- joining and fabrication processes.

When you think about processes that could be used to manufacture a new or an improved design, you need to understand how each process is carried out. Sometimes these processes will be familiar to you, such as drilling, but at other times you might need to consider a process that you have never tried for yourself, such as sand casting.

To justify if a process is suitable, you will need to do some research. Sources of information include:

- textbooks
- the internet
- your class notes.

◻ **Drilling is an example of a cutting process**

Questions to consider when deciding on processes include:

- How many products need to be made? Will it be one-off, batch or mass production?
- Which materials will be used? Not all processes are suitable for every material.
- Are there any features essential to the design that might make it impossible to manufacture using certain processes?
- What quality standards need to be met?
- How long do you have to manufacture the product?
- Are there any cost implications that you need to consider? Is there a budget that must be kept to? How do the costs of alternative processes compare?

ACTIVITY

You have previously produced a range of ideas to solve a problem. Now you need to think about how these designs could be made.

1 Which materials can be used?

2 Which processes can be used?

3 Give reasons why these materials and processes are suitable.

◻ **Folding metal with a sheet metal press**

There will be some processes that you can carry out in a small workshop, such as bending sheet metal to fabricate parts; on an industrial scale this would be done using a press, like the one shown in the photograph.

To justify the processes you have decided to use, you need to think about the following:

- How many items of the product are you planning to produce? Different processes will be needed for a one-off product compared with a mass produced product.
- Investigate processes that would be suitable for the materials you have chosen and the scale of production. For example, die casting would not be appropriate for a one-off product.
- Examine the processes used for similar products. For example, if you are redesigning the casing for a games console, look at the materials and processes used for small electrical devices.

CHECK MY LEARNING

You have investigated methods of justifying the engineering processes used to manufacture a component or product.

Working in the same pairs as in the Getting started activity, discuss alternative processes that could be used to manufacture a product or a component you looked at and give reasons for the selection of whichever process you believe to be most suitable.

Learning aim B: assessment practice

How you will be assessed

In this component, you will be assessed by completing a set task that consists of two parts, worth 60 marks in total, marked by Pearson examiners. Learning aim B is assessed mainly through Part 2 of the set task, which will take place over one and a half hours.

Part 2 will consist of two activities that target higher-order planning, redesign and evaluation skills, and which relate to given scenarios. The first section of Part 2 of the set task assesses your ability to interpret information and to use this to suggest improvements to an engineered product.

You will be assessed on how detailed your evaluation of the existing design is. If you make very basic points only, or ones that are not relevant to the problem, you will receive marks in the lowest marking band. If, however, you identify relevant issues with the design that you are presented with, and then evaluate these issues in detail to show that you fully understand the existing design and how it relates to the design brief, you will be awarded marks in the highest marking band.

Unlike in the practice activities, you will only be asked to produce one design idea in the external assessment, so you need to make sure that this one idea meets all the requirements of the brief and addresses all the areas for improvement you have identified in your evaluation.

If these aspects are not included in your responses, then you will not be able to achieve the higher marks. It is important that you annotate your work clearly to ensure that the person who is marking your designs can understand what you have done.

Remember that the examiner who will be marking your set task does not know you, and the only way they will be able to assess your engineering skills is through the work that they see you have completed.

CHECKPOINT

Strengthen
- Identify four factors that come together to form a design brief.
- Give two ways in which an engineer can vary a design to make improvements.
- Why are exploded diagrams used by engineers?

Challenge
- Explain what is meant by the term 'design for manufacture'.
- Describe two ways in which the credibility of a design can be assessed.
- Explain the reasons why engineers might use alternative components to improve a design.

You will be given a brief for an engineered product and an example of a design for the product.

You will need to evaluate the existing product to identify its strengths and weaknesses, as well as its limitations and constraints. This will be completed during the first part of the set task.

Your teacher will give you an example of an engineered product, along with details of how the product has been manufactured. Using this information, you will need to:

1 Explain the issues with the design of the product.

2 Think about how the product is made and how it will be used.

3 Annotate the drawing of the product to identify any issues.

Note: You will use your evaluation to help you redesign the product for the second part of the set task.

TIPS

When you begin your analysis of the existing product, make sure you add annotations to the drawing to explain how the product has been made, the problems you have identified with the product, and parts of the design that you think could be improved.

TAKE IT FURTHER

To gain the higher marks for this assessment, you need to make sure that the issues you identify with the existing design are relevant. You should justify these by making reference to the given drawing and the design brief.

Use technical engineering language when writing your justification and always make links with the design brief.

Analysing engineering information associated with the problem

Engineers use a combination of different types of information to manufacture an engineered product, including specific details of manufacturing processes, to ensure that the product is made to the correct size and from the correct materials.

LINK IT UP

Refer to Component 1: Learning aim B for information on quality requirements and quality control.

Types of engineering information

Engineering information can include work instructions, production data/plans, job cards, test reports and engineering drawings.

Work instructions

Work instructions describe how a part or component should be manufactured. They provide information on how to complete a task one step at a time.

Some manufacturer's manuals include information similar to work instructions, such as describing how to repair, assemble and test an engineered product by following step-by-step instructions.

Production data/plans

When manufacturing a component in a workshop, it is likely that you will use a production plan to guide you through the various stages that need to be completed. This ensures that you do not miss out any stages or complete them in the wrong order.

The complete process is broken down into stages, known as operations. Descriptions are given for each stage or operation of the process and will include information about:
- the required materials and components
- the tools and equipment to be used
- **speeds** and **feeds** to be used on machines, such as drills, lathes or milling machines
- quality control checks to be completed
- timings for each operation.

KEY TERMS

Speeds and **feeds** refer, respectively, to the 'spindle speed' (the speed at which a machine spindle rotates) and the 'feed rate' (the rate at which a machine tool moves across a 'workpiece', i.e. the material being machined).

Job cards

A job card is a form of work instruction (see Figure 3.23), as is an operations sheet. Engineering organisations use job cards as a way of showing all the requirements that need to be carried out for an activity. This may include the tools, materials and components needed, the amount of time that the activity should take, staffing details, and other details about the tasks to be completed.

Works Order No:		
Part no: Description:	Sales order no:	
Customer name:	Customer standards apply:	
Customer acc no:	Certificate of conformity required:	
Customer ref:	Check issue:	
Quantity:	Check drawing:	
Required by:		
Scheduled for:	Issued by:	
Scheduled completion:	Signature:	
Materials: Req qty Item code	Product description	
Mat spec Issued qty	Batch no Initials	

◻ **Figure 3.23: An engineering job card**

When using production documentation, you should make sure that:
- you read and understand the information fully and use it to select the correct materials, tools and equipment
- you follow the instructions in the correct order
- you ask for further guidance if you are not sure about anything.

ACTIVITY

Following the details on an instruction sheet you are given, such as a job card, produce a small engineered component by doing the following:

1 List all the materials, tools and equipment needed.
2 Obtain the materials needed.
3 Access the tools and equipment needed.
4 Follow the instructions to manufacture the component.

Test reports

A test report must be completed when an engineered product or component needs to meet specific performance requirements. You can use test reports to help identify patterns and trends within production activities.

CHECK MY LEARNING

You have looked at some types of engineering information that can be used when carrying out an engineering activity.

With a partner, discuss how you would use work instructions, production plans, job cards and test reports.

Types of engineering working drawing

We have looked at how engineering drawings can be used to present ideas and communicate information to other engineers and customers. In most cases, you will need to use a combination of drawing types to be able to communicate a design clearly.

In addition to the different formats of drawing, there are specific types of working drawing that can be used to provide particular details of a design.

Component drawings

A component drawing includes the information needed to make that particular component, including the materials to be used, dimensions of the component, any surface finishes that are required, and information about specific processes, such as producing threaded holes or counterbores. Examples of components that component drawings are generally used for include nuts, bolts, screws, integrated circuits, rivets and mechanical components such as bearings and gears.

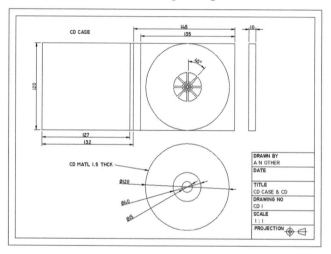

◘ Figure 3.24: Example of an engineering component drawing

Component drawings, such as the one shown in Figure 3.24, must be sufficiently clear for an engineer other than the designer to be able to follow. These drawings contain the minimum information needed to produce the part. They do not show how individual components interact or combine with each other. For this, you need an assembly drawing.

Assembly drawings

To show how component parts fit together, you need an assembly drawing. Assembly drawings, such as the one shown in Figure 3.25, are used by engineers to make sure they do not assemble components in the wrong way. These drawings do not, however, show individual details of components, and therefore assembly and component drawings need to be used together.

There are variations of assembly drawings that may be needed when developing an improved solution to a problem. These include:
- sub-assembly drawings that show how components fit together to form a larger component such as an alternator, which is a sub-assembly of a car engine assembly

- fabrication assembly drawings that show details of joining methods required for structures manufactured from sheet materials, and may also include details of welds or fixings.

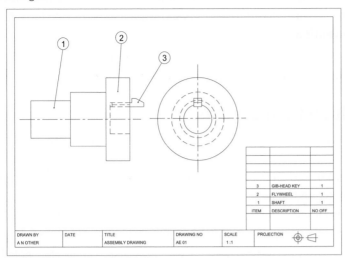

■ Figure 3.25: Example of an engineering assembly drawing

Repair and modification drawings

Sometimes repairs or modifications need to be made to a component. For example, additional holes may need to be drilled, or part of a component removed, to allow it to fit within an assembly. In these instances, there is only a need to produce a modification or repair drawing with details of the specific changes required.

Installation diagrams

Installation diagrams are used to show how a component should be installed in its final location – for example, how to install a hot water boiler or piece of machinery.

Wiring diagrams

Wiring diagrams are similar to circuit diagrams, except that they show how electrical circuit components, such as switches and other electrical equipment, are actually connected together. You can find examples of these types of diagram for the wiring of the machinery in a workshop.

ACTIVITY

Imagine that you have been tasked with designing a prototype digital camera that is suitable for water sports.

1 Research the types of drawing that you will need to use.

2 Prepare a presentation to show what information each type of drawing will provide.

3 Include an explanation of why each type of drawing is useful.

CHECK MY LEARNING

You are now aware of some of the types of drawing an engineer could use to share information.

In a group, explain what each type of drawing shows and when each type is usually needed.

Drawings and information

Engineering drawings can contain lots of information. Often these drawings may appear confusing and difficult to interpret if you are unfamiliar with the different drawing **conventions** used.

Drawings are extremely useful for showing how parts fit together, whether the parts are male or female, and how any specific connections need to be made.

Materials and components

One easy way of remembering whether a part is male or female is to think about a nut and a bolt.

- A bolt has a thread on the outside – an external thread. Parts with an external thread are termed 'male'.
- A bolt is usually assembled with an accompanying nut, which has a thread on the inside – an internal thread. Parts with an internal thread are termed 'female'.

A working drawing, or assembly drawing, will show, where applicable, details of how male and female parts fit together. Similarly, an electronic circuit diagram will show the typical values of the components within it. These could include current, voltage and resistance values. You will need to think about these details when selecting components to use.

Dimensions

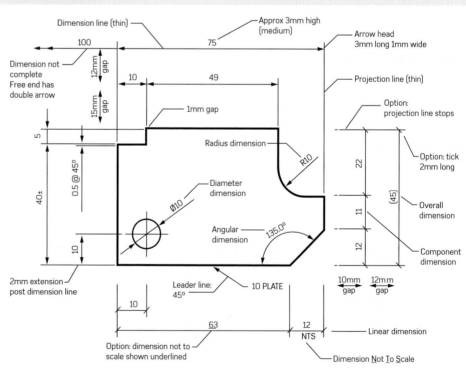

□ **Figure 3.26: Engineering drawings often include information about radii, diameters and tolerances among other manufacturing information**

Look at the example of an engineering component drawing shown in Figure 3.26. There are a range of features on the drawing that you need to understand in order to interpret correctly the information being shown.

One of the most important features of any engineering drawing is the dimensions marked on it. To interpret these, you must be able to understand the abbreviations and conventions used.

Some of the more common abbreviations and symbols are shown in Table 3.17.

◻ **Table 3.17: Abbreviations used in drawings**

Abbreviation or symbol	Meaning
⌀ or dia	Diameter
R	Radius
NTS	Not to scale

You also need to remember the following points about dimensions.

- Dimensions always show the true size of a component, although sometimes components are drawn to a different scale.
- Dimensions are usually shown only once on a drawing – this means that you may need to transfer dimensions from one side of a component to the other.
- Different line types are used for dimensioning on a component drawing – these are shown as dimension lines, extension lines and leader lines.
- Short dimensions should be labelled closest to the component – this prevents lines overlapping.
- Dimensions should never appear on top of a drawn object; they should always be to the side, away from the object.
- Try to group dimensions together wherever this is possible.
- Horizontal dimensions should appear above the dimension line.
- Vertical dimensions should be to the left or right of the line and preferably orientated so that they are written along the dimension line.

ACTIVITY

Assemble an engineered product using only engineering drawings. Make a note of any problems that you have with interpreting the drawing information and any parts of the assembly that you found easy to complete.

Take photographs, annotating them to highlight the problem areas. Discuss with a partner.

CHECK MY LEARNING

The ways in which information such as drawing dimensions and abbreviations can be added to a drawing have been covered in this lesson.

In a small group, think about and discuss the reasons why drawing conventions are important and must always be followed.

Identifying issues and causes associated with a problem

As an engineer, it is important that the products and components you design and make perform as expected. It would be inconvenient if a hook designed to hold tools in a garden shed was not able to support the weight of a spade; it could be dangerous if the tyres on a car could not cope with travelling at motorway speeds.

Identifying problems

Engineers use data from tests to identify potential problems or faults and then find solutions to these problems.

We have seen the scatter graph in Figure 3.27 previously, but what if the circled test values are accurate and not the result of measurement errors or false readings?

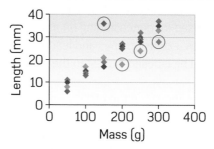

◻ **Figure 3.27: Results from a load–extension test for springs**

Looking at the graph, one of the springs extended to nearly twice the length of the others with a load of 150 g. This could lead an engineer to think that the material used is of a different quality, or perhaps of a thinner gauge than specified. By noting these anomalies in results, engineers can investigate the causes of a problem.

Typical causes of faults

Faults can be divided into two types:
● random faults
● systematic faults.

Random faults

Random faults are often associated with the materials or the equipment used to make a component. Causes of random faults include the following:

- poor-quality materials that do not meet the specification
- flaws in materials that cause the materials to fail
- blunt or damaged tools and work-holding devices
- damaged gauges and measuring equipment.

The analysis of data can help to trace random faults; for example, if a number of faulty components were produced on one machine and none on other machines, then inspections could be carried out to check for damage to that individual machine.

Systematic faults

Systematic faults are usually the result of human errors at some stage in the production process. These include:

- incorrect materials being selected for a component
- incorrect cutting speeds and feeds being used
- marking-out errors
- inaccurate use of tools and equipment.

In most cases, systematic faults will not be noticed through the interpretation of data, other than perhaps to notice trends for individual machine operators.

Interpreting patterns and trends related to engineering information

You need to be able to look at engineering information and identify whether there are patterns or trends. We have looked at the use of scatter graphs earlier, but sometimes you need more information to help identify and solve problems. For example, think about other factors such as when a component was manufactured or where it was made.

CHECK MY LEARNING

We have looked at ways of identifying problems and faults that can occur within engineering processes.

Write down as many random and systematic faults as you can think of that can impact on an engineering process.

Selecting a solution

There are many ways in which the design of a product can be improved, such as by changing the materials and/or reducing the weight or volume. However, whichever changes are made to a design, you must ensure that it will still be possible to manufacture the product.

A range of approaches can be used to make a product easier to manufacture. We have looked at some of the approaches in the lesson on using alternative components, and in many ways the approaches are similar.

◻ **Prototype of an LED torch**

With a product prototype, the materials and processes are often chosen because they are suitable for one-off production methods. This means that if the product is going to be manufactured on a larger scale, decisions will need to be made about the materials and processes to be used for the increased scale of production.

Approaches that can be taken

There are a number of aspects that you will need to consider when redesigning a product for an increased scale of production.
- Consider using standardised components.
- Design components so that they can be manufactured using as few processes as possible.
- Reduce the number of different materials in the product.
- Reduce the number of different components in the product.
- Avoid unnecessary features that do not improve the product.
- Consider the use of automated processes when selecting manufacturing methods.

Components

There are two ways in which you can redesign the componentry to make a product more efficient for manufacture.

Use of standardised components

This means using the same component in a range of products or in different combinations within the same product. In some cases, the same component can be used both in different combinations within one product and in other products.

Limit the number of different types of part in a product by standardising their design. For example, if brackets are included as part of the design, avoid having four or five different types. It is good practice to have only one design for each type of component as this reduces the time needed for processing and manufacturing and allows for ease of maintenance in the future. If there are fewer designs of a part to make, fewer tool set-ups are required, and the associated number of jigs, templates and formers can also be reduced.

Reducing the number of components

You could also reduce the overall number of components in a product. Instead of joining several parts together, consider using different processes and/or materials. For example a fabricated metal container could be replaced by a container made from injection-moulded polymers. The product can then be manufactured more quickly as fewer processes will be involved.

Materials and manufacturing processes

You should aim to reduce the number of different materials and manufacturing processes used. By limiting the range of raw materials, they can be used more efficiently and processes can be completed faster. If component parts need to be joined together using thermal processes such as welding, using the same material for all components will make assembly easier because it can be difficult to weld different metals together.

Using the same types of polymer for different components would also allow the same processes to be used to manufacture them. For example, high-density polyethylene (HDPE) could be used for various injection-moulded parts.

It is also more efficient to reduce the number of different pieces of equipment needed. The use of CNC or automated machinery should be encouraged wherever possible. These various considerations can be summarised as follows.

- Limit the number of different materials that you specify.
- Think of processes that are more efficient for manufacturing.
- Avoid using lots of different sizes and thicknesses of material.
- Think about ways in which you can include CNC processes.

ACTIVITY

Use the internet to find an image of a prototype engineered product.

1 Sketch the existing design and annotate your sketch with details about the materials used in the prototype.

2 Produce a range of 2D and 3D sketches to show how the product would be made in quantity.

3 Annotate your sketches to explain how the product would be made.

CHECK MY LEARNING

You have learned about the approaches an engineer can use to improve the design of a product by using different materials, components or processes.

With a partner, discuss the factors you need to consider when replacing a polymer material used for a prototype design with a metallic material for the actual product.

Possible engineering solutions

Think of a simple everyday product that you are familiar with. Write down any flaws or problems with the design that you can think of.

Most existing products and components, no matter how small or simple, can be improved in some way. However, producing the ideal solution is often not economic: it would cost more to redesign some components than the money an engineering company would save as a result of the design changes.

When you investigate products to identify potential improvements, you need to think about the following factors:
- the design of the product or component
- the tooling used for manufacturing the product or component
- the manufacturing processes used to make the product or component.

In most cases, improvements to one aspect of the product will have a knock-on effect on other aspects. If you change the design of a product, there are likely to be changes needed to the tooling used and potentially also to the manufacturing processes.

◻ **Example of a component that has been redesigned using computer-aided design (CAD) and then produced in titanium using 3D printing**

The component shown in the photograph, part of an axle assembly for a go-kart, was originally manufactured from stainless steel plate and then stamped out and deformed in one process.

The manufacturing company that makes this component has identified a number of faults with the existing design, including large quantities of waste material being produced and offcuts of materials that are hard to recycle.

The company decided to make some small changes to the design of the component to allow it to be manufactured using a different process. The new process chosen is 3D printing and the material has been changed to titanium. This reduces the amount of material wasted because, with an additive process, no waste materials are produced.

When you are redesigning a product, think about the concepts we have covered before and remember the acronym KISS – 'Keep It Simple, Stupid'.

Do not overcomplicate things – a simple design will probably perform better than a complex one.
- Design components so that they can be manufactured using as few processes as possible.
- Reduce the number of different materials in the product.
- Reduce the number of different components in the product.
- Avoid unnecessary features that do not improve the product.
- Consider the use of automated processes when selecting manufacturing methods.

All these factors link up with the concept of keeping the design simple.

ACTIVITY

Examine an engineered product, either a physical example or an image of one.

1 Write down any issues that you think there are with the design.

2 Make notes about any problems that you think there could be with tooling or manufacturing processes.

3 With a partner, discuss potential ways to improve the design and improve the product.

◼ Sometimes developments in technology can allow for radical changes in designs

It is possible that there are new technologies that could help simplify the product you are being asked to redesign. It is worth doing a little research to see if any new processes or technologies are being developed that would help improve your design. The image above shows what the inside of a television used to look like – think about how thin and lightweight televisions are now because of the new technologies that have been invented since then.

You also need to think about the extent to which your engineering solutions have fulfilled their primary purpose. In other words, does the solution do what it is supposed to do? For example, while a smartphone has many functions, its primary purpose is to allow people to communicate.

CHECK MY LEARNING

You have learned about methods that you could use to make a design simpler, yet still perform its primary purpose.

Working with the same partner as in the previous activity, think about another product that you are both familiar with, one that has more than one function. Discuss which approaches will lead to the greatest benefit in making the product more effective.

Wider factors that need to be considered

You may be asked to redesign a product or component that has been made as a one-off so that it can be produced in larger batches. This means that a different approach will need to be taken for the design and the manufacturing methods.

One-off production

One-off production is used either when you are making a prototype of a product or when a customer wants something that is specially made for them. Often these one-offs are made by just one person, but sometimes small groups of people will work together to produce them. In both cases, the same people work on the complete product from start to finish. One-off products are unique, which makes them expensive to produce because of the amount of time spent on manufacturing them.

Batch production

If a number of products or components are needed that are all from the same design, then they can be made in a batch. Unlike one-off production, batch production offers opportunities to use automation. The production process allows for changes to be made – for example, to make the products in a different size. Often a production line is used to make one type of product, and then the line is adapted to produce a different type of product.

◻ **Alloy wheels are an example of a batch-produced product**

Table 3.18 gives a summary of the differences between one-off production and batch production.

◻ **Table 3.18: Characteristics of one-off and batch production**

	One-off production	Batch production
Unit costs	High	Medium
Tools and equipment	General use	**Specialised equipment**
Initial investment	Low	Medium
Production efficiency	Low	Medium/high
Labour type	Skilled	Skilled/semi-skilled
Labour cost	High	Medium

Imagine you are an engineering designer. You have been asked to analyse an existing batch-produced product.

1 Investigate the materials and processes used to make the product.

2 Produce a short presentation that includes information about:

   a) resources needed

   b) reasons for batch production

   c) safety factors

   d) environmental impacts.

Environmental impacts

Environmental impacts of production must be considered when designing an engineered product. These include the following.

Use of energy during production

Energy will always be used during the production of engineered products. However, different sources of energy will have differing impacts on the environment. With fossil fuels, such as coal, oil and gas, there are impacts from the extraction of the fuel source and the burning of these fuels to produce energy. Other sources – renewable energy such as solar and wind power – can be used to generate cleaner energy. The source of the energy and the amount used are important when considering the impact of production on the environment.

Use of resources during production

It is best to avoid non-renewable materials, such as oil-based polymers, or materials that cannot be recycled at the end of their useful life.

Production waste and pollution

Try to avoid wasting materials. This can be achieved by using alternative processes such as 3D printing or casting, or through the recycling of waste materials and offcuts. Sometimes it is unavoidable that waste is produced, for example when turning a workpiece on a lathe or vacuum forming a polymer sheet to produce a moulding. The most effective way of reducing waste, though, is to make sure that production is '**right first time**'.

You have learned about some of the issues that need to be considered when designing a product for manufacture, such as the requirements of batch production and environmental issues that should be considered.

In small groups, discuss the outcomes of the investigation you carried out in the lesson activity – how would your findings impact on your redesign of the product?

Ways to improve the solution

There are many reasons why a product or component might need to be redesigned. For example, it may need to be redesigned so that it still fits another component that has also had to be redesigned, or the manufacturer might have considered that the processes used are not environmentally friendly.

Evaluating an existing design

Designers will normally be given the reasons why a product needs to be redesigned, or why the features need to be improved to make the product more effective at meeting its design requirements.

ACTIVITY

You have been asked to redesign a batch-produced shelf bracket. The manufacturer of the bracket has had complaints from customers that the bracket bends and cannot hold the loads it is designed to support.

The existing bracket is made from aluminium and is shown in the image below.

1 Use the internet to find out information about the materials and processes that are used to make the existing bracket.

2 Evaluate the existing bracket design to identify issues that could be causing it to fail and not meet the design brief.

The evaluation of an existing design will need to bring together information about various factors and review it to form a conclusion, drawing on evidence from the design brief and engineering drawings; it should include the strengths and weaknesses of the existing design.

When evaluating an existing design, you need to do the following tasks.

- Read through the original design brief for the product.
- Highlight the key points that the design must meet.
- Look at the existing design and circle features that you think could be an issue – this will ensure that you do not forget anything when you are writing your evaluation.
- Consider using subheadings in your evaluation, one for each product feature, and give reasons why you think the feature is going to be a problem. Try to include some information about each of the following factors in your evaluation:
  - physical requirements
  - aesthetics
  - size
  - function
  - performance requirements.

Remember that you need to justify your reasons and use connectives – for example: 'The bracket might not support the weight of the shelf because the material is very thin.'

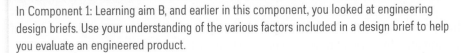

LINK IT UP

In Component 1: Learning aim B, and earlier in this component, you looked at engineering design briefs. Use your understanding of the various factors included in a design brief to help you evaluate an engineered product.

Your evaluation will help you to decide which features of the product need to be redesigned and how to plan for the production of an improved design. This process should give you an opportunity to identify limitations and constraints associated with the existing design.

- Limitations are factors that impact on how well the design functions – for example, the maximum weight that could be supported by a bracket or the number of fixings needed to keep something secure.
- Constraints include things such as materials, costs, space available for the product or other parts that it must fit together with. A USB connection lead would be useless if the plug was a different size and shape from the port it needed to plug into – for the connection to work, the lead and the plug must fit together (this is an example of a constraint).

CHECK MY LEARNING

You have learned about some of the issues to be considered when evaluating an existing engineering solution to a problem.

With a partner, look at a product that you use as part of your daily life – for example, a watch, a mobile phone or even an item of clothing – and identify the strengths and weaknesses of the product's design.

Producing an alternative design solution

You will need to use your evaluation of an existing product to develop an alternative design solution that meets the requirements of the design brief. It is a good idea to think about different approaches before starting to sketch out designs on paper.

We have already looked at methods that can be used to redesign a product or component, but some of these approaches are not always suitable. In the case of a support bracket, like the one in the previous lesson, we cannot simplify the design by reducing the number of components because it has only one component to begin with.

ACTIVITY

Look at an existing engineered product that you have evaluated previously and think about the following:

1 How could the performance of the product be improved?

2 What could be changed to make the design more effective?

3 Can the materials be changed?

4 What alternative processes could be used?

When producing an alternative design solution, you will need to answer these types of question and think about how you could include all these factors in a design solution.

You need to produce design ideas that:

- meet the design brief in full
- show an improvement on the original design
- include justifications of the alternative design solution – this will link to your evaluation
- include justifications of the processes to be used in manufacturing.

Remember that if you are asked to produce one design idea only, you need to ensure that your idea meets all the requirements of the design brief and addresses all areas of improvement that you have proposed in your evaluation.

It is important that you annotate your design work clearly to ensure that other people can understand what you mean and the design features intended.

Justification of your solution

It is normal for the **justification** of the proposed solution to be presented in a written report, so you need to ensure that points are made clearly and linked to both the design brief and your evaluation of the existing design.

> **KEY TERM**
>
> **Justification** is the reason or evidence to support an idea or design.

You will need to choose a solution based on the advantages and disadvantages of each design idea. As we have seen before, this could be done by checking how much of the design brief is met by each of the ideas and how much of a variation from the original design your new proposal would involve. Make sure you show links between the disadvantages of the existing design and the advantages of your improved new design. Remember to support your comments with reasons.

You could use a best-fit approach to select the best solution. This is similar to the RAG rating that we looked at earlier. You will need to consider the strengths and weaknesses of each of your design ideas and compare them against the design brief.

Some aspects of a design brief are more important than others, so you should identify a solution that meets all the criteria satisfactorily.

Your solution should show that you have a good understanding of engineering theory and processes.

When you are generating initial ideas, think about any limitations or constraints associated with the design. Does the design solution have to fit in a certain space or does it need to be a particular colour? You must be sure that your improved design meets all the constraints that are given.

As a further example of a constraint, suppose that the shelf bracket previously mentioned must have three holes to attach it to a wall, and these must be in the same location as the existing holes.

Finally, you should also identify the limitations of your design; for example, if you plan to make the product from medium carbon steel, then a protective coating will be needed, otherwise it will corrode.

> **CHECK MY LEARNING**
>
>
>
> You have learned about some of the factors that need to be considered when justifying a design solution. With a partner, discuss the following questions:
>
> 1 How can you check if a design meets the brief?
>
> 2 Why is material choice important?
>
> 3 How can you support the decisions that you make?

Reflecting on your design solution

We have looked at some of the things that you need to consider when justifying your design solution, including the reasons for your choice of design idea. You also need to justify the approach you propose to take for manufacturing the new design.

When selecting materials for the redesigned product, there are a number of factors that you should think about:
- material properties
- material cost and availability
- the processes that you plan to use
- the environment.

Material properties

There will be an expected level of performance from the material selected so that it will do the job it is designed to do. This could be related to the mechanical properties of the material, such as strength or durability. If the material properties are not suitable for the purpose, then the product or component will fail.

LINK IT UP

Go to Component 2: Learning aim A for information on material properties.

Material cost and availability

The cost of materials that you plan to use must be appropriate for the product. While materials such as titanium might offer improved properties compared to mild steel, if, for example, the application is a coat hook, then the cost of titanium is probably too high.

Materials must also be readily available; there is little point in specifying a material that cannot be easily obtained.

Processes to be used

Selection of materials must be linked with how you intend to manufacture the product; for example, which cutting, shaping, forming, and joining and fabrication techniques are you considering? The material choices must be suitable for the processes you plan to use.

LINK IT UP

You have investigated a range of cutting, shaping, forming, and joining and fabrication techniques in Component 2: Learning aim A.

The environment

You need to think about where the product is to be used and the effect that the environment will have on the product; for example, a shelf made from polymer materials would not be suitable for use inside an industrial oven.

Conversely, you also need to think about the effect that the materials and the manufacturing processes used will have on the environment. Casting, for example, uses a lot of energy to heat the materials. However, very little waste is produced during the casting process. You will need to weigh the advantages and disadvantages of using a particular material against the environmental impacts.

Another environmental factor to consider is whether it is possible to reuse or recycle waste produced either during the manufacturing process or at the end of the life of the product.

Making recommendations for improvements to the best solution

Your selection of the best manufacturing process to use is also important because it needs to be suitable for the product you are designing. You will need to make recommendations for improvements to allow the best solution to be produced.

Consider the advantages and disadvantages of alternative processes; for example, a coat hook could be cast in aluminium, or it could be formed by cutting and then bending strips of aluminium. The process chosen will need to take into account the scale of production, such as whether the component needs to be made in a batch, and the complexity of the design. The most important thing to remember is that you must always be able to justify your decisions.

ACTIVITY

Review your chosen design solution for an improved engineered product.

1 Justify your choices of materials.

2 Justify your choices of manufacturing processes.

Make sure that you link your justifications to the improvements you have suggested for the design as well as the original design brief for the product.

CHECK MY LEARNING

You have investigated some of the factors that need to be considered when making decisions about the materials and manufacturing processes to be used to improve an engineered product.

With a partner, discuss the following questions:

1 Why are the properties of a material important when making decisions about its use?

2 Why does the environment need to be considered when choosing and justifying a design solution?

3 What factors can influence the choice of processes?

Resources required and their use

Having selected your design solution, you then need to think about specific details of the solution, especially the resources required to produce the product. These resources include the materials, tools and tooling, components, equipment and apparatus needed.

Materials

It is not only the type of material that is important, but also the form of supply, the sizes needed and any surface finishes or textures that will be required. Materials can be supplied in a range of forms, depending on the material category, as shown in Table 3.19.

◘ **Table 3.19: Material forms of supply**

Metals	Polymers and composites
Ingots	Powders
Castings	Pellets
Forgings	Extrusions
Pressings	Mouldings
Bars or rods	Sheets
Sheets	Resin
Plate	Films
Pipe or tube	Pipe or tube
Wire	
Rolled sections	
Extrusions	

Tools and tooling

The types and forms of selected materials will affect the tools and tooling that need to be used. For example, if polymers are selected for the product, and they are to be supplied in pellet form, then the manufacturing processes that can be used will be limited, with injection moulding being the most likely choice.

In reality, decisions about materials, their forms of supply and manufacturing processes will be made jointly as each decision impacts on the others. The decision about the most suitable methods for manufacturing a component will take into account the features that need to be produced; this in turn will have implications for tooling. If die casting is suggested, then a die will need to be produced and metal heated until it melts and can be poured. If a turning process is suggested, then a lathe will be needed, along with appropriate cutting tools depending on the type of metal being turned and the features to be produced (see Figure 3.28).

The choice of tools and tooling also needs to be suitable for the scale of production expected.

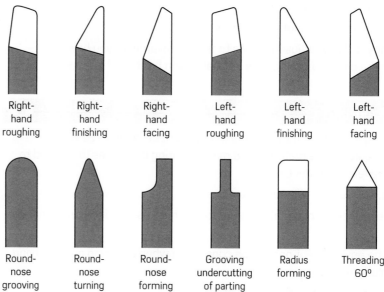

Right-hand roughing   Right-hand finishing   Right-hand facing   Left-hand roughing   Left-hand finishing   Left-hand facing

Round-nose grooving   Round-nose turning   Round-nose forming   Grooving undercutting of parting   Radius forming   Threading 60°

◘ **Figure 3.28: Lathe tools should be selected depending on the feature to be produced**

Components

Components have been considered at a number of stages in the design process. However, when deciding on the components to be used for a redesigned or improved solution, the choices may not be that simple.

You need to ensure that, if necessary, any alternative components are compatible with the existing design. This is especially important if the new component is a replacement for an existing, different component. It may still be possible to standardise on the type of component – for example, using the same type of screw head or standard dimensions and values of electronic components.

Equipment and apparatus

Sometimes there will be a need to use specialist equipment or apparatus when producing a redesigned product or component. It might be that specific instruments will need to be used to check the surface finish of a component, or sensors will need to be used to check if an electronic circuit has the required levels of sensitivity.

The equipment resources to be considered might include work-holding devices such as machine clamps to hold workpieces in place when they are being milled or drilled; soldering irons and related hand tools for soldering activities; or measuring equipment to ensure that components fit together as specified.

ACTIVITY

You have been asked to plan the manufacture of an engineered component that has features that need to be produced by either milling or turning.

1 Carry out some research into the tools and equipment that will be needed, and list these.

2 Write a short report to explain and justify your choices of resources.

Example

To manufacture a redesigned shelf bracket, mild steel could be chosen as the material and shearing, drilling and bending processes used to shape it. Specifying a standardised drill size (e.g. 8 mm) allows standard components to be used, and using a jig ensures that all brackets will be bent to the correct angle.

CHECK MY LEARNING

You have learned about the resources that you are likely to need when manufacturing an engineered product. With a partner, make a list of the following types of resources for the manufacture of an engineered product you are familiar with:

- materials
- tools and tooling
- components
- equipment and apparatus.

Presenting your solution

In addition to justifying a design solution and the processes and materials that you plan to use, it is important to consider the methods that can be used to present the solution.

When selecting presentation methods, you will need to consider a range of techniques and decide which will be the most appropriate. These can include both sketching and formal presentation drawings. We have looked at each of these in detail earlier in this component.

Drawings

An isometric drawing, as in Figure 3.29, allows the features of a design to be shown in three dimensions so that another engineer or a potential user can visualise what it will look like in real life.

One of the limitations of isometric drawings is that they do not always provide enough information for someone to produce a product or component directly from them. Often, you will need to use another drawing or document to provide the full information.

If the idea you have produced is complicated, it might be better to use an isometric drawing to show the overall shape and form of the design proposal and also use orthographic projections to show details of the design features.

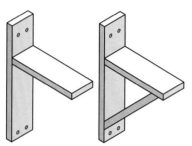

■ Figure 3.29: Isometric drawing of a redesigned shelf bracket

An orthographic drawing, as in Figure 3.30, allows construction details to be added, such as dimensions, both linear and angular, and notes about surface finishes and joining methods.

Remember that when producing an orthographic drawing, you need to ensure that details are absolutely clear.

You will also need to use the correct line types for hidden details, outlines, centrelines and dimensions. Don't forget that you should always show dimensions in millimetres (mm).

Also think about the scale of the drawing. If the product or component is small, then it may be better to produce a drawing to a larger scale, one which shows the item at a larger size than in real life.

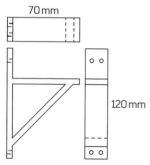

70 mm

120 mm

■ Figure 3.30: Orthographic drawing of a redesigned shelf bracket

You have investigated the use of CAD software to produce drawings in Component 1: Learning aim B.

Think about the methods used to present 3D CAD models, and try applying these same approaches in your presentation of ideas.

Annotations

Annotations are very important in design work. You must ensure that you add appropriate annotations to design information so that they clearly explain:

- the features of your solution and how it meets the design brief
- the materials and processes that you would use, including the reasons why
- details of how the solution will work; for example, if there are any moving parts, then explain how these will operate.

You have practised different methods of presenting an engineering design using different kinds of drawing.

Working with a partner, look at ways in which your drawings could be improved. Some starting points you could think about are:

- accuracy
- the amount of detail included
- size and scale.

Make processes to create a prototype solution

When developing a new product, there are a number of reasons for making a prototype, including:

- trialling ideas to see if they work as expected
- testing a product to check that it functions as intended
- gaining a better understanding of the problem.

There are different ways of producing a prototype, including the use of rapid prototyping and traditional physical modelling.

Processes to follow and use

You will need to think about processes in relation to using tools and equipment, health and safety, and manufacturing processes like casting, forging, welding and the use of jigs and tools.

3D printing – additive manufacture (AM)

You could create a CAD drawing of a component and then send this to a 3D printer to be manufactured. This enables an accurate model of the design to be produced, which can then be used to test whether or not the design would work. It is even possible to produce 3D printed models with parts that move.

You should experiment with and practise producing accurate CAD drawings of engineered components. If a 3D printer is available, use simulation software to view the models onscreen and then manufacture the component.

Physical modelling

A physical model can be made using a range of modelling materials. These include card, wood, plastics and parts reclaimed from disassembled products.

As already considered in Component 1: Learning aim B, 3D models may be viable if they are made by hand. Prototype models can be made easily from materials that are easy to shape and easy to modify.

In some cases, you can produce a model that incorporates 3D printed parts, with other aspects of the design made using traditional physical modelling methods.

◨ Different materials can be used to produce models for the same solution

If prototypes for the same design are made from different materials, it can help with the selection of material forms and manufacturing techniques.

Following correct processes

Whenever you are modelling or carrying out any part of an engineering investigation, you should follow the correct processes. Think about manufacturing on a larger scale and for the actual product. This could involve casting, forging and welding, along with the use of other tools and jigs. You may need to research how certain processes are carried out and whether they are suitable for your design.

It is especially important to follow correct procedures when using tools and equipment. You should only ever use tools and equipment that you have been given permission to use and shown how to use safely. The engineering saying, 'If in doubt – ask!' applies to all parts of an engineering activity: if you are not sure how to do something, then ask for help.

Also ensure that you work safely at all times and follow the health and safety rules for the equipment you are using. Remember to follow instructions and use the correct PPE to carry out each process.

Collecting and analysing data

GETTING STARTED

With a partner, make a list of the types of data that could be collected from engineered products. Discuss which of these types of data can be used to improve outputs.

We have already looked at the collection of data from engineering activities, including the dimensions of components, and methods for determining whether or not a component is within specified tolerances.

Collecting data

ACTIVITY

Collect at least ten of the same type of component or product that nominally have the same dimensions – for example, machine screws or mass-produced components such as injection-moulded bottle lids.

1 Measure and record the dimensions of each of the components you collected.

2 Plot the dimensions of the components on a line graph.

3 Write a short summary report to explain your findings.

◨ Table 3.20: Example of data collected for a component that has a required length of 25 mm

Test number	Length measurement (mm)
1	25
2	25
3	25
4	23.5
5	27
6	26
7	24
8	27
9	26
10	23

Once you have collected and recorded your data, as shown in Table 3.20, for example, plot the measurements on a line graph. This will help you to identify any trends or patterns.

The raw data do not show trends easily. However, by plotting the points on a graph, you can spot if there are any patterns or erroneous values that need to be investigated further.

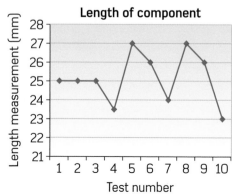

◨ Figure 3.31: Chart showing the results from Table 3.20 in inspection order

Although the data shown in Figure 3.31 are representative of the results found in the sequence of tests during the inspection, it can be more useful to present the data in a more logical way.

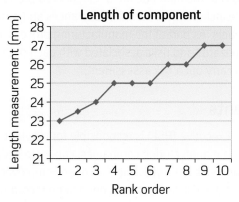

■ Figure 3.32: Chart showing results in rank order

Looking at the two ways of presenting the same data, the graph in Figure 3.32 allows us to see more easily that three components are smaller than the nominal length and four components are longer than the required length.

Quantitative and qualitative data types

Quantitative data relate to information that is expressed in numbers, such as an item's height, the number of products, or the length of a component, like the example in Table 3.20. These are numerical quantities that can be measured.

Qualitative data give information about a product's characteristics, and are used to describe features of an item, such as the colour or shape of a product. These data are difficult or impossible to measure and are not expressed in terms of numbers. However, if you were to count, for example, the number of red products, then the data would become quantitative.

In engineering, data collected for analysis of statistical trends and patterns generally fall within the quantitative data type, but both types of data are useful and important to know about.

Analysing data

Analysing the results in Figures 3.31 and 3.32 does not really show any trends, so it is more than likely that the differences in size are down to marking-out errors or operator mistakes.

Remember to present your data in a way that is easy to interpret. It is generally a good idea to present data in rank order so that any trends and patterns can be identified more easily.

We looked at the causes of faults in production earlier in Component 3, and classified faults as being either random or systematic. It is much easier to identify systematic faults, and therefore devise solutions for this type of fault, than to identify random faults, so this is where efforts need to be concentrated. A systematic fault will usually give rise to a pattern or trend.

You should analyse data, first, to decide if faults are random or systematic and, second, to think about solutions to the problem.

CHECK MY LEARNING

You have examined different sets of data and looked at the methods used to present data to make them easier to interpret.

Think about the best way to present each of the following types of data:

- the length of time taken to set up a pillar drill
- the number of faults in an electronic circuit
- the actual measured resistance values of resistors.

Safety considerations

All aspects associated with the manufacture of engineered products will have some elements of risk. These include the materials, substances and processes used to manufacture the products. As part of the manufacturing process, it is important that you are aware of the hazards and risks associated with each of these. One way of approaching this is to carry out a risk assessment.

Risk assessments

The Health and Safety Executive (HSE) is responsible for regulating workplace safety. All employers, including manufacturing companies, can try to keep their employees safe by conducting and using risk assessments. For any employer that has more than five members of staff, these risk assessments need to be recorded in writing.

The HSE recommends that a risk assessment is carried out in five steps:

1 Identify the hazards.

2 Decide who might be harmed and how.

3 Evaluate the risks and adopt associated control measures.

4 Record and action your significant findings.

5 Review your assessment and update if necessary.

An example of a risk assessment is set out in Table 3.21.

Remember that for hazardous substances, you should make sure that control measures meet with the requirements of COSHH (Control of Substances Hazardous to Health) Regulations 2002.

You should also think about the length of time people will be exposed to risks; for example, ear defenders are acceptable for short-term exposure to noise, but for long-term exposure, a permanent method of reducing noise would be better.

LINK IT UP

Each stage of the risk assessment process has been explained in detail in Component 2: Learning aim B. It is important that all stages of the process are completed in full and are accurate in detail.

■ Table 3.21: Example of a risk assessment

What are the hazards?	Who might be harmed and how?	What are you already doing?	What further action is necessary?	Action by whom?	Action by when?	Done
Tools on the floor in an untidy workshop	Staff or visitors to the workshop might trip over or slip on the tools on the floor causing serious injury	Daily housekeeping at the end of the shift	Better housekeeping – ensure tools and equipment are cleared away immediately after use and not left until the end of the day	Production supervisor	Now	01/09/17
			Improve tool and equipment storage in the work area	Site maintenance manager	14/09/17	01/09/17

Investigate the materials and processes you have proposed for use in the manufacture of your chosen design solution.

1 Carry out a risk assessment to identify hazards and decide who might be harmed.

2 Identify suitable control measures.

3 Record your risk assessment in a suitable format.

■ The use of appropriate PPE is one way of providing control measures for machine operators

PPE should not be relied on as the only type of control measure for hazards.

Wherever possible, you should try to eliminate hazards. If this is not possible, see if you can use alternative materials or methods that pose less of a risk.

Considering timescales

You will need to be aware of the timescales that you have to keep when designing an improved engineering product. You will only have a limited amount of time in your external assessment, so you will need to manage this time well. You should avoid spending too much time on one activity, and make sure you attempt each part of the assessment activity.

You have thought about the hazards that can be present during an engineering process and you have investigated control measures, including the use of PPE.

With a partner, write out a risk assessment for one engineering process, such as a turning operation on a lathe. When you have finished, compare your risk assessment with that of another pair in your class group – are there any risks or actions they included that you didn't? Think about and discuss the reasons for any differences.

Learning aim C: assessment practice

How you will be assessed

In this component, you will be assessed by completing a set task that consists of two parts, worth 60 marks in total, and marked by Pearson examiners. Learning aim C is assessed mainly through Part 2 of the set task, which will take place over one and a half hours.

Part 2 will consist of two activities that target higher-order planning, redesign and evaluation skills and which relate to given scenarios. In the set task you will show that you understand how to interpret information and use this to suggest improvements to an engineered product.

You will be assessed on how detailed your evaluation of the existing design is. If you make very basic points only, or ones that are not relevant to the problem, you will receive marks in the lowest marking band. If, however, you identify relevant issues with the design that you are presented with, and then evaluate these issues in detail to show that you fully understand the existing design and how it relates to the design brief, you will be awarded marks in the highest marking band.

Unlike in the practice activities, you will only be asked to produce one design idea in the external assessment, so you need to ensure that this one idea meets all the requirements of the brief and addresses all the areas for improvement you have identified in your evaluation.

If these aspects are not included in your responses, then you will not be able to achieve the higher marks. It is important that you annotate your work clearly to ensure that the person who is marking your designs can understand what you have done.

Remember that the examiner who will be marking your set task does not know you, and the only way they will be able to assess your engineering skills is through the work that they see you have completed.

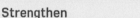

CHECKPOINT

Strengthen
- Identify four types of engineering drawing.
- Give two reasons why engineers make prototypes.
- Why do engineers use risk assessments?

Challenge
- Explain the difference between a random fault and a systematic fault.
- Describe two approaches to improve an engineering solution.
- Explain why it is important to consider scale of production when improving a design.

ASSESSMENT ACTIVITY | LEARNING AIM | C

In the first section of Part 2 of the set task, you were given a brief for an engineered product and an example of a design for the product. You then evaluated the existing product and identified its strengths and weaknesses, as well as its limitations and constraints. You will use this evaluation to help redesign the product for this second section of Part 2 of the set task.

Your teacher has previously given you an example of the engineered product, along with details of how the product was manufactured. Using this information and your previous evaluation, you need to:

1 Produce one idea for the product that shows an improvement on the original design.

2 Justify why your design idea is an improvement and explain which processes you would use to make the redesigned product.

TAKE IT FURTHER

When you explain the processes that you would use to make your design idea, you should justify their use by taking into consideration the materials that you have chosen, the intended purpose and function of the product, and also the scale of production, if this is included in the brief.

TIPS

When you redesign the given engineered product, make sure that the design shows an improvement on the original and that you justify your design solution fully.

Draw your designs clearly and make sure that all the details are shown. Sometimes it is better to draw a number of 2D views rather than produce only one 3D drawing.

Glossary

Abrasion the process of wearing something away.

Accuracy depends on the way in which measurements are taken and how they are recorded.

Alloys mixtures of two or more metals that have improved properties and characteristics.

Ancillary equipment covers any items of equipment required by the main equipment system to be a complete system.

Annotations labels used by engineers to give information about designs.

Annual turnover the amount of money relative to the value of the products and services a company sells over a year.

Assembly drawings used to show how components are put together.

Assembly line a process where engineers and machines assemble a product in a specified sequence.

Axis the name of either the horizontal or the vertical line that is used to show the scale of the graph or chart.

Blind hole a hole that does not break through to the other side of the workpiece.

Blow moulding a manufacturing process by which hollow plastic parts are formed.

Brainstorming an open group discussion of ideas to find solutions.

Branding of a product or company name is a way of distinguishing it so that it is easily recognisable.

Capacitors electronic devices that store electrical charge.

Chamfers features that remove sharp corners to make something safer and easier to assemble.

Chargehand a worker put in charge of others.

Chartered engineer registered with the Engineering Council as a person who has academic qualifications, technical training and knowledge, and practical experience. They are permitted to use the abbreviation CEng after their name.

Charts usually used when data are being presented in groups.

Chuck a specialised kind of clamp.

CNC stands for 'computer numerical control'. A CNC lathe is one that runs automatically.

Cold working when a material is reshaped while at a low temperature.

Commissioning the final testing and verification of the equipment's functionality.

Complex brackets brackets that have been designed for a specific purpose and often have complicated shapes that allow them to fit around other components but still remain strong.

Composite materials formed when two or more materials are bonded to produce a material with different properties from the original materials.

Compressible when the volume of a fluid can change when pressure is applied to it.

Compressive strength the ability of a material to resist a pushing force without being crushed.

Conductivity the ability of a material to conduct electricity.

Conductors materials that transmit heat or electricity.

Conform and **conformance** both mean meeting specified standards, regulations or laws.

Control valves automatic devices used to control fluids in a pipe.

Conventions the rules used to present information such as drawings; for example, BS8888 is the standard set of rules for working drawings. They cover line types, symbols and layouts of drawings.

Customised parts engineering products made or modified to meet the customer's specified requirements.

Deadline the latest date that the solution of a problem, e.g. an engineered product, needs to be completed by.

Degree of accuracy half a unit on either side of the unit of measure; if the unit is 1, then any measurement between $9\frac{1}{2}$ and $10\frac{1}{2}$ will be measured as 10.

Die a tool used to create a specific shape as part of the manufacturing process. A die is custom made for each specific job so that an exact shape can be made.

Diodes electronic devices that can be used to allow electrical charge to flow in only one direction.

Ductility the ability of a material to be deformed by bending, twisting or stretching. This ability increases in metals at higher temperatures.

Electroplating a process in which an electrical current is run through a solution between a zinc anode and a steel conductor.

Engineered products items produced using suitable engineering production processes.

Engineer's blue a quick-drying ink used to help the marking-out process on metals.

Ergonomics the science associated with the design and arrangement of equipment so that it is more comfortable and safer for people to use.

Ethical something that is morally good or right to do.

Fabrication the process of manufacturing something.

Feedback when you receive information, good and/or bad, from someone else about what you have done.

Ferrous metals contain iron. Typical types of ferrous metals include mild steel, wrought iron and stainless steel.

Fettling trimming or cleaning the edges of a metal casting.

Fillets similar to radii, but feature on internal corners and are used to reduce stresses in a joint.

Fit-for-purpose term used to describe whether a product can perform the job it was designed to do.

Fluid a gas or liquid.

Fuselage the main body of an aircraft, where passengers sit or freight is carried.

Galvanising the process of providing a protective zinc coating to steel. Products tend to be hot-dipped to provide the coating.

Graphs used to plot individual data values.

Gyroscopes wheels or discs that spin freely on their axes to find their orientation by themselves.

Handover possession of the equipment is passed to the customer.

Hazards things that could be dangerous to someone's health and safety.

Hot working when a material is reshaped while at a high temperature.

In-house activities are carried out by employees of the company.

Indentation the process of making a notch or scrape in a material.

Integrity the quality of having moral principles.

Interconnection the close connection between, or the joining of, two or more things.

Interpretation an opinion of what something means; when you interpret something, you are deciding what you believe to be the meaning.

Iteration repeating a process until the best solution is identified.

Justification the reason or evidence to support an idea or design.

Labelling used to identify groups of data clearly.

Lathes tools that rotate a workpiece to perform functions such as shaping, cutting and sanding.

LED stands for 'light emitting diode' and produces light when a voltage is applied to it.

Lifespan a product refers to how long it will last once a consumer begins using it for its primary purpose.

Logistics the organisation and implementation of an operation, usually involving a lot of detail.

Longevity a long life.

Machine shop where engineers use machine tools and cutting tools to make parts.

Malleability the ability of a material to be permanently deformed in all directions without breaking apart.

Marketplace a term used to describe the activities associated with the sale and purchase of a product.

Milling machines used to shape materials, but the material is fixed and the cutting tool rotates.

Nanotechnology the branch of engineering technology that deals with extremely small things, including the manipulation of atoms and molecules.

Non-compressible a fluid that cannot be compressed.

Non-ferrous metals do not contain iron. Typical non-ferrous metals include aluminium, titanium, copper, silver and zinc.

NVQ stands for National Vocational Qualification: a practical qualification gained through employment.

Orientation of an object is its direction or relative position.

Outsourced functions are carried out by someone outside the company.

Parts integration the ability to combine different parts.

Patent the sole right of a person or company to make or sell a product.

PDF stands for portable document format and is used for creating electronic documents.

Permanent something intended to last unchanged forever.

Pilot hole a small hole drilled ahead of a full-sized hole as a guide.

Plating a thin coating of gold, silver or other metal.

Precision the depth of information that is included in the data: how far the information is broken down.

Products things produced for sale, usually by a manufacturing process.

Qualitative comparisons a type of analysis used when the data collected are circumstantial (very detailed).

Quality control the set of procedures that are followed to ensure that the quality of a product is maintained and manufacturing errors reduced or eliminated.

Radius (or **radii**) refers to a smooth, rounded corner, like a chamfer, typically used on external corners.

Recesses internal grooves, also known as pocket cuts.

Recycling the process of converting waste material into other usable products.

Re-forming changing something from one shape to another.

Reliability depends on there being only small variations in data and that measurements are within tolerance.

Resistance to wear means that something is not easily damaged over time.

Resistors electronic devices that restrict the flow of an electric current.

Resolution a term used to describe how clear an image is.

Right first time often quoted in terms of quality control and refers to when something is done without errors so that no time and money are wasted.

Risers occur where excess metal from the moulding escapes from the casting box. They will also solidify, and so need to be removed at the end of the process.

Risk the probability of a hazard causing harm to someone's health.

Risk assessment a process used to document that all hazards have been considered and appropriate measures put in place to deal with them.

Runners used to allow metal to flow from one moulding to another so that multiple parts can be cast at the same time.

Rusting when a metal becomes covered in a reddish-brown, flaking coating of iron oxide. Rusting affects iron and steel.

Scale the ratio of the model compared to its actual physical size. For example, if a model is ten times smaller than in real life, the scale of the model is 1:10.

Sector a term used for a particular type of industry within the nation's overall economy.

Semi-permanent something will not last forever, but will last for a long time.

Services the actions of providing something for a customer, usually performing work or a process.

Setpoints target values for a process value, e.g. maximum temperature, minimum flow rate.

Shank the shaft of a tool.

Shear force arises from forces that act in opposite directions.

Skill set the range of skills and abilities that a person has.

Specialised equipment can be used for more than one product or component, but can only be used to carry out a limited range of processes.

Speeds and **feeds** refer, respectively, to the 'spindle speed' (the speed at which a machine spindle rotates) and the 'feed rate' (the rate at which a machine tool moves across a 'workpiece', i.e. the material being machined).

Sprue the hole that molten metal is poured into when casting. When the casting solidifies, the sprue needs to be removed.

Surface roughness a measure of the deviations of a real surface from its ideal form. If these deviations are large, the surface is rough; if they are small, the surface is smooth.

Sustainability the ability of something to be maintained at a specific level.

Swarf the small chips or pieces of metal removed by machining processes such as grinding, turning or milling.

Team building a method of getting employees to work together as an effective team.

Teeth the grooves on engineering tools.

Tensile something is capable of being stretched out.

Tension the pulling force or forces on an object.

Thermosetting polymers materials that cannot be reshaped with the application of heat. Typical thermosetting polymers include phenol-formaldehyde, polyimides and polyurethane.

Thermoforming polymers materials that can be reshaped with the application of heat. Typical thermoforming polymers include polyethylene, polypropylene and acrylic.

Thinking outside the box to think in an original or creative way.

Thread a raised structure on a screw or bolt that follows a helical path and allows parts to be joined together.

Tolerances the allowable variation of a specified dimension, normally associated with machining operations but can also apply, for example, to equipment that needs to be set up exactly level for it to operate correctly.

Transparent polymer allows light to pass through it in such a way that objects behind it can be easily seen.

Trends patterns in data, e.g. values might increase for one variable as the values decrease for another.

Troubleshooting the identification and correction of faults and problems.

Unit cost the cost of one item, e.g. if 10 m of pipe costs £20, the unit cost is £2 per metre.

Unit costs the costs associated with the manufacture of an individual product.

Vanishing points points on an imaginary horizon where all projection lines in a perspective drawing are drawn from.

Velocity the object's direction and speed of movement.

Virtual reality computer technology that uses special equipment such as headsets to create images, sounds and other sensations that simulate a user's physical presence in a virtual or imaginary environment.

Welding heating the surfaces of two objects to the point of melting and then joining them together.

Workpiece a piece of metal or other material that is in the process of being worked (cut or shaped) by a hand tool or machine.

Index